Joan V. Cooper.
April 1949.

THEORY OF EQUATIONS

UNIVERSITY MATHEMATICAL TEXTS

GENERAL EDITORS

ALEXANDER C. AITKEN, D.Sc., F.R.S.
DANIEL E. RUTHERFORD, Dr. Math.

Determinants and Matrices	Prof. A. C. Aitken, D.Sc., F.R.S.
Statistical Mathematics .	Prof. A. C. Aitken, D.Sc., F.R.S.
Waves	Prof. C. A. Coulson, Ph.D.
Integration	R. P. Gillespie, Ph.D.
Infinite Series	Prof. J. M. Hyslop, D.Sc.
Integration of Ordinary Differential Equations	E. L. Ince, D.Sc.
Analytical Geometry of Three Dimensions	Prof. W. H. M'Crea, Ph.D.
Functions of a Complex Variable	E. G. Phillips, M.A., M.Sc.
Vector Methods	D. E. Rutherford, Dr. Math.
Theory of Equations	Prof. H. W. Turnbull, F.R.S.

Other volumes in preparation

THEORY OF EQUATIONS

BY

H. W. TURNBULL, M.A., F.R.S.
REGIUS PROFESSOR OF MATHEMATICS IN THE UNITED COLLEGE,
UNIVERSITY OF ST ANDREWS

With 25 *Figures*

OLIVER AND BOYD
EDINBURGH AND LONDON
NEW YORK: INTERSCIENCE PUBLISHERS, INC.
1947

First Edition 1939
Second Edition, Revised 1944
Third Edition, Revised and Enlarged . 1946
Fourth Edition, Revised 1947

PRINTED AND PUBLISHED IN GREAT BRITAIN BY
OLIVER AND BOYD LTD., EDINBURGH

PREFACE

This book is founded on the lecture course given in the University of St Andrews to students reading for an Ordinary Degree in Mathematics and to first-year Honours students. It contains a short and elementary account of algebraic equations, both from the theoretical and the practical side, together with the algebra of polynomials and rational fractions. It includes classes of number, partitions, identities, the G.C.M. process, partial fractions and recurring series, but it omits continued fractions and indeterminate equations. Cubic and biquadratic equations are discussed, together with more general types, elimination, and symmetric functions, but the theory of invariants and of groups is left untouched.

An elementary knowledge of algebra is presupposed, particularly of long division, quadratic equations and the binomial theorem, together with elementary determinants, coordinate geometry and differential calculus. The more advanced determinantal and matrical theory of p. 48 and p. 141 may be omitted on a first reading.

The book has been written with the historical development of algebra constantly in mind; and many of the topics have been selected for their importance, not only as part of a general mathematical education, but also as preliminaries to the study of all higher algebra.

I acknowledge with gratitude the help which I have derived from the well-known treatises on algebra and equations written in England, Ireland, America and Germany: more particularly from the works of Todhunter and of Professor P. B. Fischer. I also thank the editors of the present series, my colleagues, and the printers for their helpful co-operation.

H. W. TURNBULL.

PREFACE TO THE SECOND EDITION

THE text of the first edition has been revised, and I am grateful to friends who have pointed out to me various errors, which have been corrected in the present edition. A new chapter is added on general methods of root expansion, which links the early work of Newton with recent discoveries of the Edinburgh School of Algebraists, and affords an introduction to the study of bialternants.

H. W. T.

CONTENTS

CHAPTER I

INTEGERS, MORE GENERAL TYPES OF NUMBER, POLYNOMIALS

CHAPTER II

CONTINUITY AND EVALUATION OF POLYNOMIALS

CHAPTER III

THE THEORY OF RATIONAL FUNCTIONS

CHAPTER IV

THE FUNDAMENTAL THEOREM OF ALGEBRA

CHAPTER V

PROPERTIES OF THE COEFFICIENTS OF AN ALGEBRAIC EQUATION

CHAPTER VI

TRANSFORMATION AND NUMERICAL SOLUTION OF ALGEBRAIC EQUATIONS

CHAPTER VII

THE LOCATION OF THE ROOTS OF AN EQUATION

CHAPTER VIII

BINOMIAL AND RECIPROCAL EQUATIONS

CHAPTER IX

THE CUBIC EQUATION

CHAPTER X

THE BIQUADRATIC OR QUARTIC EQUATION

CHAPTER XI

ELIMINATION OF THE UNKNOWN FROM CONSISTENT EQUATIONS

CHAPTER XII

FURTHER LIMITING AND APPROXIMATE PROCESSES

CHAPTER I

INTEGERS, MORE GENERAL TYPES OF NUMBER, POLYNOMIALS

1. Integers and Partitions. The concepts of positive integers and of their partitions are fundamental in algebra. We may imagine the natural numbers 1, 2, 3, ... to be arranged in a sequence, as here, according to ascending order of magnitude. The nth term of the sequence is the positive integer n. For every integer n there is an integer $n+1$ immediately following ; so that the complete sequence of natural numbers has no last term. We may express this by saying that no positive integer is infinite, or in symbols by writing $0<n<\infty$.

If $r, s, \ldots, z$ are k positive integers such that

$$n = r+s+ \ldots +z \quad . \quad . \quad . \quad (1)$$

then k must be some number between 1 and n inclusive, so that $1 \leqslant k \leqslant n$. If n is fixed we may regard (1) as an equation to determine the unknowns $r, s, \ldots, z$. Usually there are several possible solutions and the equation is said to be indeterminate ; but if $k = 1$ there is one solution $r = n$, and if $k = n$ there is again one solution, $r = s = \ldots = z = 1$. The set $\{r, s, \ldots, z\}$ is called a partition of n, and it is customary to arrange the parts, or terms, $r, s, \ldots, z$ in ascending, or else in descending, order. For example $\{112\}$ is a partition of 4 into $1+1+2$, and $\{346\}$ of 13 into $3+4+6$. Derangement of the terms is immaterial, so that we should reckon $1+2+1$, $2+1+1$ or $1+1+2$ to be the same *partition*. It is easy to verify that there are five distinct partitions when $n = 4$:

$$\{1\ 1\ 1\ 1\}, \quad \{1\ 1\ 2\}, \quad \{1\ 3\}, \quad \{2\ 2\}, \quad \{4\}. \quad . \quad (2)$$

These are sometimes represented graphically by

$$\begin{array}{ccccc} \times & & & & \\ \times & \times & & & \\ \times & \times & \times & \times\times & \\ \times, & \times\times, & \times\times\times, & \times\times, & \times\times\times\times, \end{array} \qquad . \quad . \quad (3)$$

where rows of crosses take the place of *parts* or terms in the partition. In general the top row has r crosses, the second, s, ..., and the last, z. We may naturally enquire how many distinct partitions of n exist: and if we denote this number by $p(n)$, we can verify that $p(1) = 1$, $p(2) = 2$, $p(3) = 3$, $p(4) = 5$, $p(5) = 7$, but to find an expression for the general value $p(n)$ proves to be a singularly difficult undertaking, which has taxed the skill of the greatest mathematicians.

The five partitions of $n = 4$, arranged as above, are said to be in lexical order. This manner of arrangement becomes obvious when the integers 1, 2, 3, ..., are replaced by the respective letters a, b, c, ..., and each partition is regarded as a "word," for then the words fall into alphabetical, or lexical, order: *aaaa, aab, ac, bb, d*. Such an order is possible and unique for each value of n.

Conjugate Partitions. The partitions {112} and {13} are said to be conjugate. Conjugacy is a mutual relation which becomes intuitive when the graphs of crosses are examined: the columns of one graph, read from left to right, have the same numbers of entries as the rows of the conjugate graph read from below to above. Conjugate graphs are therefore reflexions of each other in a line inclined at 45° to the rows or columns. Every partition possesses a conjugate or else is *self-conjugate*: {1111} and {4} are conjugate, {22} is self-conjugate.

Example.—Obtain the partitions of $n = 5$, $n = 6$, and arrange them in conjugate pairs, and self-conjugate singles.

2. Rational and Irrational Numbers. In a more

general view, integers are either positive, negative or zero, and can be arranged in ascending order . . . -3, -2, -1, 0, 1, 2, 3, ... If n is any such integer then $-\infty < n < \infty$. If p is any integer and q is any positive integer, the number $p \div q$ (or p/q) is a *rational* number, a concept which leads at once to the theory of fractions, proper and improper, of factors, multiples, prime numbers and pairs of numbers prime to one another (that is, which have no common factor other than unity), with all of which terms it will be supposed that the reader is familiar. By expressing a rational number in decimal form we may find that it either terminates or recurs: for example $241/100 = 2{\cdot}41$ which terminates, while $12/11 = 1{\cdot}090909... = 1{\cdot}\dot{0}\dot{9}$ recurs. Conversely, every terminating or recurring decimal is reducible to a rational number of the form p/q, and when p and q are prime to each other the reduction is unique. But we may also contemplate decimals which neither terminate nor recur, such as $0{\cdot}1234567891011...$ (which is composed of the digits of the positive integers in natural order), or $1{\cdot}4142... = \sqrt{2}$. These represent *irrational* numbers. We include under the name *real* both rational and irrational numbers. As it is impossible to make a complete list in ascending order of all the consecutive rationals (much less of irrationals) between two integers, it is natural to invoke the help of geometry and to represent these numbers by points on a straight line. Each real number x is then represented by a point N upon an unlimited axis X′OX, and x is called the coordinate of N referred to an origin O: and the number x is the distance ON in terms of a given unit distance.

3. Polynomials, Equations, Complex Numbers. We may consider numbers from another point of view as the roots of equations. If n is a positive integer the expression

$$f(x) \equiv a_0x^n + a_1x^{n-1} + a_2x^{n-2} + ... + a_{n-1}x + a_n \quad . \quad (1)$$

is called a *polynomial* of order or *degree* n in the variable x (briefly, an n-ic in x), whose coefficients a_0, a_1, ..., a_n are constants, of which a_0 is non-zero ($a_0 \neq 0$). The relation $f(x) = 0$ is then called an *equation* of order or degree n. It is a major problem of mathematics to determine the roots of this equation, that is, to find values of x for which the equation is true. The attempt to solve the equation—to find one or more such roots—has led to the concept of a new type of number, distinguishable from the real, and called a *complex* number.

Let us write out the equation systematically for low values of n, using a, b, c for the coefficients:

$$\begin{aligned} &ax+b = 0, \qquad a \neq 0, \\ &ax^2+bx+c = 0, \\ &ax^3+bx^2+cx+d = 0, \\ &ax^4+bx^3+cx^2+dx+e = 0, \end{aligned} \qquad . \quad . \quad . \quad (2)$$

and so on. These are called the linear, quadratic, cubic, quartic (or biquadratic), ..., equation respectively. First let all the coefficients be integers: then the linear equation is soluble in rationals, namely $x = -b/a$. Conversely every rational number is the root of a linear equation with integer coefficients; for example 2·41 is the root of $100x = 241$. In particular if $a = 1$ the root of such an equation is an integer. Rational roots may also exist for higher equations, as in $2x^2-3x+1 = 0$, of which $x = 1$ is a root, or in $x^3-3x-18 = 0$, of which $x = 3$ is a root; but in general the roots of non-linear equations are irrational. Even with integer coefficients a, b, c the quadratic equation $ax^2+bx+c = 0$ cannot always be solved unless complex numbers are introduced. For the elementary method gives the formal solution

$$x = \frac{-b \pm \sqrt{(b^2-4ac)}}{2a}, \quad a \neq 0, \quad . \quad . \quad (3)$$

which is only possible in terms of real numbers when $b^2-4ac \geqslant 0$. If b^2-4ac is a perfect square p^2, >0, there are two solutions $x = -(b \pm p)/2a$ which are both rational. If b^2-4ac is positive but not a perfect square there are two irrational solutions. If $b^2-4ac = 0$ there is one solution ; it is rational, and the quadratic is said to have a repeated root. But if b^2-4ac is negative there is no real solution : and at one time in the history of mathematics such an equation was rejected as impossible. However, the more enterprising of mathematical pioneers—Cardan, Napier, Wallis, Leibniz and Gauss—boldly went forward, asserting the existence of a new type of number, which Napier called the ghost of a real number but which nowadays is called the *complex* number. The formula (3) gives two complex values of x whenever $b^2-4ac<0$, that is when $4ac-b^2$ is positive. It is usual to reduce x to the form

$$x = \alpha \pm i\beta, \qquad . \quad . \quad . \quad (4)$$

where $\alpha = -b/2a$ and $\beta = \sqrt{(4ac-b^2)}$, so that both α and β are real, but i is not real, although it satisfies the quadratic equation with real coefficients,

$$i^2+1 = 0. \qquad . \quad . \quad . \quad (5)$$

Here we have made two important assumptions :

(i) that equation (5) has a root i (which can formally be written $\sqrt{-1}$),

(ii) that this root i is a number which combines with the real numbers according to the ordinary laws of algebra.

Example.—The equation $2x^2+x+3 = 0$ has complex roots $-\frac{1}{4}+i\frac{\sqrt{23}}{4}$; so also has $2x^2+6x+5 = 0$, the roots of which are $-1\frac{1}{2}\pm\frac{1}{2}i$.

4. Geometrical Treatment of Complex Numbers. There are several ways of justifying the above assumptions regarding complex numbers, but perhaps the most

attractive, and on first consideration the most convincing method, is that of Gauss (1797), who represented a complex number $a \pm i\beta$ by a point (a, β) referred to rectangular Cartesian axes Ox, Oy in the familiar way.

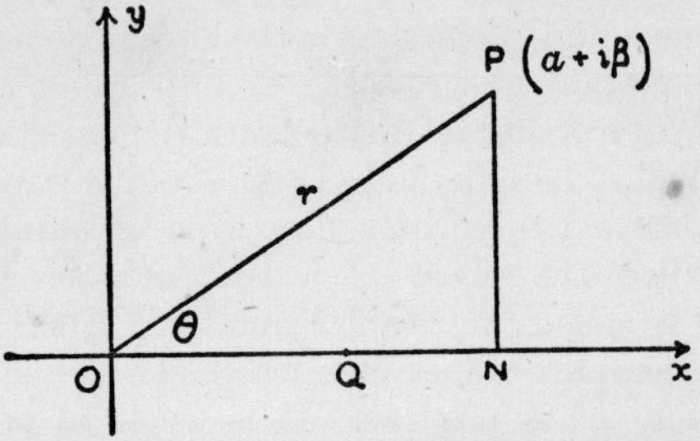

To each point P of a plane there correspond a number pair (α, β) and a complex number $\alpha + i\beta$. There is thus a one-to-one correspondence between the finite points of the plane and the finite complex numbers. The plane is called the *complex number plane*, the *Gauss plane* or, sometimes, the *Argand diagram*.

In polar coordinates $\{r, \theta\}$ we have $\alpha = r \cos \theta =$ ON, $\beta = r \sin \theta =$ NP and therefore

$$\alpha + i\beta = r(\cos \theta + i \sin \theta). \quad . \quad . \quad (1)$$

We may always avoid any ambiguity by assuming that

$$r \geqslant 0, \ -\pi < \theta \leqslant \pi. \quad . \quad . \quad . \quad (2)$$

With these provisos, which attach to each complex number one value of r and one of θ, we call r the *modulus* and θ the *amplitude* of the number $z = \alpha + i\beta$ represented by the point P. The notation $|z|$ is used for the modulus. Thus

$$|z| = |\alpha + i\beta| = r = |\alpha - i\beta|. \quad . \quad . \quad (3)$$

Also $\tan \theta = \beta/\alpha$ or am $z = \text{arc} \tan \beta/\alpha = \tan^{-1} \beta/\alpha$. . (4)

Real numbers are represented by points on the axis of x or by number pairs of the type $(\alpha, 0)$, where α can be positive, negative or zero. Pure imaginary numbers $i\beta$ are represented by points on the axis of y, except the origin (0, 0), or by number pairs of the type $(0, \beta)$, where $\beta>0$ or $\beta<0$. For this reason the line $y = 0$ is sometimes called the *real axis* and the line $x = 0$ the *imaginary axis.*

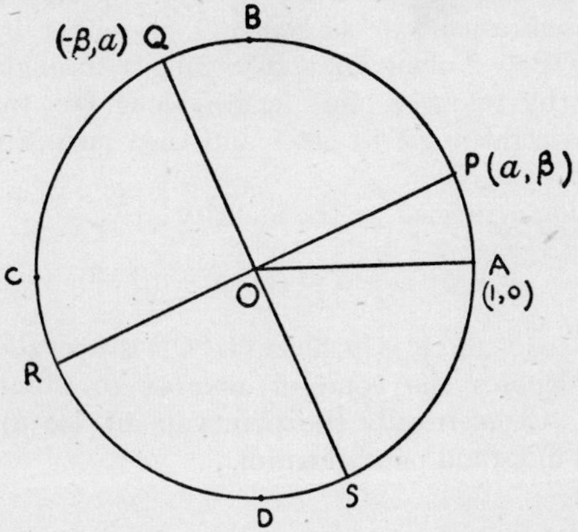

The symbol i is to be regarded and defined as an operation upon real numbers which changes the real pair (α, β) on which it operates to $(-\beta, \alpha)$, or geometrically, the operator i is defined as that which turns the line OP in a positive sense to OQ *through a right angle.* In the figure of a circle PQRS, ignore the points ABCD for the moment, and suppose the radius r to take any positive value.

From this definition everything follows. Repeat the operation and OP is turned to OR through two right angles: three operations iii turn OP through three, and four operations $iiii$ through four right angles. If $z = \alpha+i\beta$ then the four expressions iz, $iiz = i^2z$, $iiiz = i^3z$, $iiiiz = i^4z$ denote the four complex numbers corresponding to Q, R, S, P, the vertices of a square centred at O, for all non-zero values of z. We note that $i(ii) = (ii)i = iii$.

In particular if $z = 1$ and P is at A, then i, i^2, i^3 are written short for $i1$, $i^2 1$, $i^3 1$ and correspond to the points B, C, D respectively. But C has coordinates $(-1, 0)$; hence $i^2 = -1$. This links the present definition of i with the previous assumption, that i denoted the root of the equation $i^2+1 = 0$.

Next we can show that $i\beta$, βi mean the same number. For both correspond to the point $(0, \beta)$—either by taking a length OP $= \beta$ along Ox and turning it through a right angle, or by taking a unit length along Ox, turning it through a right angle to get i and then measuring off β such units along Oy.

Addition is defined by the identity

$$\alpha+i\beta+\gamma+i\delta = (\alpha+\gamma)+i(\beta+\delta). \qquad (5)$$

If P is (α, β) and R is (γ, δ) and OPQR is a parallelogram, then Q denotes the complex number so obtained by addition. Geometrically the points $(0, 0)$, (α, β), (γ, δ), $(\alpha+\gamma, \beta+\delta)$ form a parallelogram.

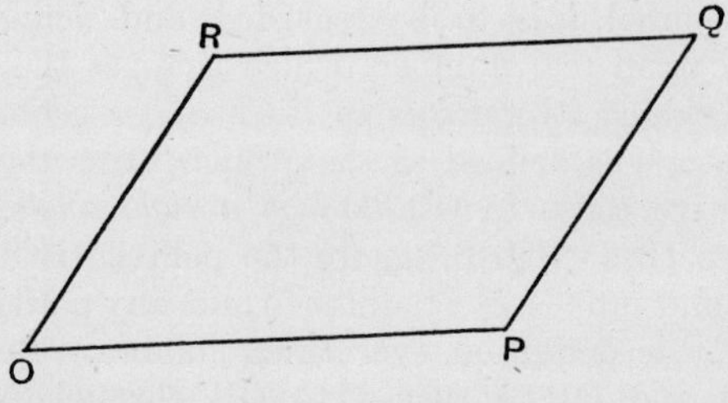

Subtraction follows at once as the inverse of addition. If we write, for short, $\overline{OP}+\overline{OR} = \overline{OQ}$, then $\overline{OQ}-\overline{OP} = \overline{OR}$. Or, again, replace γ and δ by $-\gamma$ and $-\delta$ in the above, and we have

$$\alpha+i\beta-\gamma-i\delta = (\alpha-\gamma)+i(\beta-\delta). \qquad (6)$$

Multiplication is defined by the identity

$$(\alpha+i\beta)(\gamma+i\delta) = \alpha\gamma-\beta\delta+i(\alpha\delta+\beta\gamma) \quad . \quad (7)$$

which is readily formed by the ordinary rules of algebra, and the relation $i^2 = -1$, but is geometrically equivalent to the following rule :

Let the corresponding polar coordinates be $\{r, \theta\}$ and $\{s, \phi\}$. Then

$$\{r, \theta\}\{s, \phi\} = \{rs, \theta+\phi\}, \quad . \quad . \quad . \quad (8)$$

that is, multiply the moduli and add the amplitudes to get the modulus and the amplitude of the product. If $\theta+\phi>\pi$ or $<-\pi$, the amplitude is of course the equivalent angle between $\pm\pi$.

To prove that this rule is equivalent to the identity (7) we take, as is usual,

$$\alpha = r\cos\theta,\ \beta = r\sin\theta,\ \gamma = s\cos\phi,\ \delta = s\sin\phi \quad (9)$$

and thus we can write $(\alpha, \beta) = \{r, \theta\} = r(\cos\theta+i\sin\theta)$ to denote the same complex number. Hence

$$\begin{aligned}(\alpha+i\beta)(\gamma+i\delta)\\ &=r(\cos\theta+i\sin\theta)s(\cos\phi+i\sin\phi)\\ &= rs(\cos\theta\cos\phi-\sin\theta\sin\phi+i(\cos\theta\sin\phi+\sin\theta\cos\phi))\\ &= rs(\cos(\theta+\phi)+i\sin(\theta+\phi)),\end{aligned}$$

or $(\alpha, \beta)(\gamma, \delta) = \{rs, \theta+\phi\}$, which is what we wished to prove. The rule given above for forming the product of two complex numbers is in fact a geometrical statement of Demoivre's theorem.

Division is defined as the converse of multiplication, namely,

$$\{r, \theta\}\div\{s, \phi\} = \{r/s, \theta-\phi\}, \quad s\neq 0, \quad . \quad . \quad (10)$$

for, by the earlier rule,

$$\{r/s, \theta-\phi\}\{s, \phi\} = \left\{\frac{r}{s}s, \theta-\phi+\phi\right\} = \{r, \theta\}.$$

Manifestly $\{r, \theta\}\{s, \phi\} = \{s, \phi\}\{r, \theta\}$.

It is well to notice that this rule of multiplication incorporates the earlier geometrical definition of i. Instances of (7) are

$$\{2, 0\}\{1, \tfrac{1}{2}\pi\} = \{2, \tfrac{1}{2}\pi\},$$

$$\{3, \tfrac{1}{2}\pi\}\{2, -\tfrac{1}{2}\pi\} = \{6, 0\}, \{1, \tfrac{1}{2}\pi\}\{1, \tfrac{1}{2}\pi\} = \{1, \pi\},$$

that is to say, $2\times i = i2$, $3i\times(-2i) = 6$, $i\times i = -1$.

5. Complex Numbers as Roots of Quadratic Equations. The number $\alpha+i\beta$ is a general complex number, separated into real and imaginary parts α, $i\beta$ respectively. Sometimes β is referred to, rather loosely, as the *imaginary part* of the complex number. We note that every such complex number is a root of a quadratic all of whose coefficients are real: for if $x = \alpha+i\beta$ then $(x-\alpha)^2 = (i\beta)^2 = i^2\beta^2 = -\beta^2$. Hence $x^2-2\alpha x+\alpha^2+\beta^2 = 0$, which is a real quadratic equation. Similarly, $\alpha-i\beta$ is a root. We call these two roots *conjugate complex* roots, and we say that $\alpha\pm i\beta$ form a pair of conjugate complex numbers.

The sum of two conjugate complex numbers is always real, the difference (whenever $\beta\neq 0$) is a pure imaginary.

We have introduced complex numbers by going no further than quadratic equations whose coefficients are integers. The questions naturally arise, what happens if we allow the coefficients themselves to be fractional, irrational or even complex, and again if we consider equations of higher degree ? It is one of the dramatic surprises of mathematics to find that no further generalization is necessary, in that any such equation can be completely solved in terms of complex or simpler numbers. This fact, which is called the fundamental theorem of algebra, was first proved by Gauss (*cf.* p. 56). At present we shall assume it, and shall illustrate its scope by two examples.

1. To solve the complex linear equation $ax+b = 0$, where a and b are complex. Let $a = \alpha+i\beta$, $\bar{a} = \alpha-i\beta$; then

calculate $x = -b\bar{a}/a\bar{a}$. For instance if $(2+3i)x+4-5i = 0$, we have

$$x = \frac{5i-4}{2+3i} = \frac{(5i-4)(2-3i)}{(2+3i)(2-3i)} = \frac{7+22i}{4-9i^2} = \frac{7}{13}+\frac{22}{13}i.$$

The point of the process is to render the denominator real and thus to separate the real and imaginary parts of x. We *realize* the denominator of a complex fraction by a method analogous to that of rationalizing the denominator of a surd.

2. Every polynomial whose coefficients are complex can be regarded as a factor of a polynomial whose coefficients are real. For example: $(2+i)x^2-(3+2i)x+i$. Arrange this as $(2x^2-3x)+(x^2-2x+1)i$ and multiply it by the conjugate polynomial $(2x^2-3x)-(x^2-2x+1)i$, obtained by changing i to $-i$. The result is

$$(2x^2-3x)^2+(x^2-2x+1)^2,$$

or $5x^4-16x^3+15x^2-4x+1$, which is real.

6. Algebraic Numbers and Integers. Within the scope of real and complex numbers further demarcations can be made. If $a_0 \neq 0$ and each coefficient of the polynomial in **3** (1) is an integer, then each root, real or complex, of the equation $f(x) = 0$ is called an *algebraic number*: conversely any such number must be a root of such an equation for a finite value of n. In particular if $a_0 = 1$, each root is called an *algebraic integer*: for instance i is an algebraic integer. So also is $\sqrt{3}$, for it is a root of $x^2-3 = 0$; and again the complex surd $\omega = (-1+i\sqrt{3})/2$ is an algebraic integer, for it is a root of the equation $\omega^2+\omega+1 = 0$. The numbers $\pm i$ are sometimes called the *imaginary units*, for they have properties resembling those of the real units ± 1. In fact if $x = \pm i$ or ± 1 then any integral power of x is equal to one or other of these four units.

Algebraic numbers may be rational or irrational, but it does not follow that all irrationals are algebraic: such as are not so are called transcendental, well-known examples of which are $\pi = 3{\cdot}1415926535...$ and $e = 2{\cdot}7182818284....$

Neither of these is the root of an equation of finite degree, whose coefficients are integers. The first attempt to prove the transcendence of π and e was made in 1667 by James Gregory, but the first strict proof was given by Lindemann as recently as 1882.

Note.—The arithmetical foundations of the theory of rational and irrational numbers is due to Dedekind and Cantor. For a full treatment of real and complex numbers the reader is referred to G. H. Hardy, *Pure Mathematics* (Cambridge, 1938), pp. 1-33.

7. Rational Functions. By an obvious extension of ideas we classify functions of a variable x in much the same way as numbers, into integral, rational, irrational, algebraic and transcendental functions. The result of combining x with itself and with constant numbers by addition, subtraction and multiplication in any order, with or without repetitions, but *only with a finite number* of such elementary operations, is called a *rational integral function*. It is in fact a *polynomial*, which can always be arranged in descending powers of x. If division is also admitted a finite number of times the function is called a rational, but it may be *fractional*, function. Practice with these processes will have convinced the reader that any such function can be reduced to one or other of the forms

$$f(x)/\phi(x), \quad f(x), \quad c,$$

where both $f(x)$ and $\phi(x)$ are polynomials in x, and c is a constant, which may possibly be zero.

Examples.

(i) $\dfrac{1}{1+\dfrac{2}{x}}+x$, (ii) $\dfrac{x^2-1}{x-1}$, (iii) $(x+a)(x-a)-(x+b)(x-b)$.

(i) Here $f(x) = x^2+3x$, $\phi(x) = x+2$; (ii) $f(x) = x+1$; (iii) $c = b^2-a^2$.

Examples of polynomials or rational integral functions :

$2x+3$, x^3, ax^2+bx+c, $\frac{1}{4}x^2-3$, $(px-q)^3+rx$, $2x^n+3x^p-1$, where n and p are positive integers.

Rational fractional functions :

$$\frac{1}{x}, \frac{a+bx}{c+dx}, \frac{2-3x+4x^2}{x^2}, \frac{1-x^n}{1-x^{2n}}, \frac{1}{x-1}-\frac{2}{x-5}, x^{-3}-2x^{-4}+x.$$

Irrational functions : $\sqrt{x}$, $\sqrt[3]{(x^2-2)}$, $(1+\sqrt[3]{x})/(1-x)$.

Transcendental functions : e^x, $\sin x$, $\log x$, $\sin^{-1}x$.

The above examples are typical but not exhaustive. The functions also may be either algebraic or transcendental, so that we include under algebraic both rational and irrational cases. The feature of an algebraic function $y = \psi(x)$ is that it is always possible to express the relation between x and y rationally as a polynomial involving both variables, say $f(x, y) = 0$. For example,

$$\text{if } y = (1+\sqrt[3]{x})/(1-x), \text{ then } (y(1-x)-1)^3-x = 0.$$

This is called a *sextic* equation in x and y, since the term of the highest degree is x^3y^3. It is impossible to express a transcendental function by such an equation of finite degree.

Further examples. Discuss the nature of the following functions: $\sqrt{(x^2+2x+1)}$, $\sqrt{(x^2+1)}$, $(1-x)\sin^2 x/(1-\cos^2 x)$, $(x^2+2x)/x$. [Rational, irrational, polynomial, polynomial.]

8. Tabular and Graphical Representation of a Polynomial. If $f(x)$ is a given real polynomial of degree n, and if $y = f(x)$, then it is always possible to represent the function $f(x)$ both graphically and by means of a table. We take particular values $x_1, x_2, x_3, \ldots$ of x and calculate the corresponding values $y_1, y_2, y_3, \ldots$ of y. Since $f(x)$ is rational, integral and real, we obtain one real value of y for each x. Had $f(x)$ been a rational fraction this would not be the case, for there would be no value of y corresponding to such exceptional values of x as cause a denominator to vanish. The results can then be tabulated either by rows or by columns in the familiar way, and when this is done the table gives a representation of the function. While it is a suggestive and useful representation, yet it is only approximate, for the values of y are usually decimalized and accurate only to a limited number of decimal places, and in any case a complete set of values in any interval whatever is out of the question. It is useful to arrange the values of x from left to right, or else columnwise, in ascending order.

Example. $y = f(x) = x^3 - x^2 - 4x + 4.$

x	-10	...	-3	-2	-1	0	1	2	3	4	5	6	...	10
y	-1056	...	-20	0	6	4	0	0	10	36	84	160	...	864
			A	B	C	D	E	F	G	H				

However full the table is, it is always possible to increase it, either by extension or by interpolation. By the latter is meant inserting new values of x between adjacent values of x already found, yielding the corresponding y. What, in this example, are the values of y within the interval $1 < x < 2$? For each such value of x it will be found that y is negative.

Tables such as these were familiar to the mathematicians of the sixteenth and early seventeenth centuries, who developed great skill in devising methods for elaborating them : their aim was to render tables of trigonometrical and logarithmic functions as complete as possible. But a great advance in insight was gained in 1638 when Descartes published his method of coordinates, whereby any such table could be thrown into geometrical form by plotting points A, B, C, ... whose coordinates were x and y, one such point for each pair of entries. These points are distinct and separated : they form a discontinuous graphical representation of the function. They do not lie at random, but suggest a curve which runs smoothly through them in the order indicated from left to right.

The greater the number of entries in the table within any given interval AH the more clearly will the corresponding points suggest a curve : and whatever smooth curve is drawn through them it will be an approximate representation of one precise curve which *par excellence* represents the function. Suppose that this precise curve is

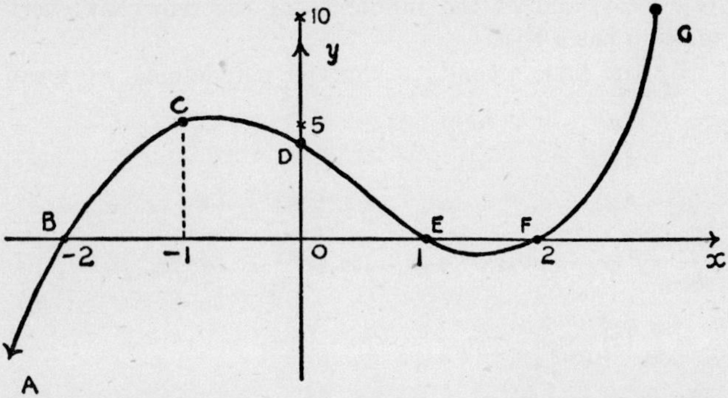

drawn through the points ABC... ; it will be such that whatever pair of corresponding values x, y are taken, the point P representing them will lie on the curve. We shall call this the graph of the polynomial $f(x)$, or the curve whose equation is $y = f(x)$, or briefly the curve $y = f(x)$.

Every polynomial with real coefficients has such a graph. The curve extends indefinitely to the left and to the right. It must cut any straight line drawn parallel to the axis of y in one point and one point only, since y takes one definite value for each value of x. The curve is continuous, as will shortly be proved; it has no gaps. Its curvature is continuous; it has no sudden corners, but bends smoothly. It crosses a straight line drawn parallel to the axis of x not more than n times. If $n = 1$ it is a straight line. If $n = 2$ it is a parabola, upwards or downwards, $\cup$, $\cap$ with its axis parallel to Oy. Such a curve, we say, has one bend. If $n = 3$ it has two bends. If $n = 4$ it has one or three such bends. If $n = 5$ it has two or four. In general if $n = 2r$ it has an odd number of bends less than n, and if $n = 2r+1$ it has an even number of bends less than n. For the purpose of drawing polynomial graphs, or of visualizing them, these are useful facts to bear in mind. The reasons underlying them depend on the properties of the derived polynomials $f'(x)$, $f''(x)$, and of the fundamental theorem that every equation has a root.

By the first, second, ... derived polynomials we mean

$f'(x) = \frac{dy}{dx}$, $f''(x) = \frac{d^2y}{dx^2}$, and so on. Thus

$$y = f(x) = a_0x^n + a_1x^{n-1} + a_2x^{n-2} + \ldots + a_{n-1}x + a_n,$$

$$\frac{dy}{dx} = f'(x) = na_0x^{n-1} + (n-1)a_1x^{n-2} + \ldots + 2a_{n-2}x + a_{n-1},$$

$$\frac{d^2y}{dx^2} = f''(x) = n(n-1)a_0x^{n-2} + (n-1)(n-2)a_1x^{n-3} + \ldots + 2a_{n-2},$$

and so on. Each such derivative is a polynomial of degree less by unity than its predecessor. Accordingly the $(n-1)^{th}$ derivative is a linear polynomial, while the nth derivative is the constant $d^ny/dx^n = n!\, a_0$, which is non-zero. All higher derivatives must vanish.

Example.

$$y = f(x) = x^3 - x^2 - 4x + 4,\ y' = f'(x) = 3x^2 - 2x - 4,$$
$$y'' = f''(x) = 6x - 2,\ y''' = f'''(x) = 6,\ f^{IV}(x) = 0.$$

CHAPTER II

CONTINUITY AND EVALUATION OF POLYNOMIALS

9. Continuity of a Polynomial Function. Let (x, y) be the coordinates of a point P, regarded as fixed, which lies on the polynomial graph $y = f(x)$. Let Q be another point $(x+h, y+k)$ also on the graph, so that $y+k = f(x+h)$. We shall say that the function $f(x)$ is continuous at x if we can make k as small as we please by taking h small enough. More precisely, if ϵ is a given positive number however small, then k must lie between $-\epsilon$ and ϵ (that is $-\epsilon < k < \epsilon$) whenever h lies between $-\eta$ and η, where η is a positive number (usually small) which can be ascertained when ϵ is given. This statement, a little difficult at first sight, turns out on reflection to agree with our idea of continuity for a curve; but it has the merit of giving in precise quantitative form a test for what seems to be a qualitative property. Since a value of y exists for each value of x there can be no gap in the curve as traversed from left to right; but there might conceivably be one or more gaps vertically. Suppose, in such a case, that P is the last point on the curve before such a gap, and Q the first point after the gap; then we have merely to choose ϵ less than the distance PQ in order to show that such a curve does not fulfil the quantitative test just given.

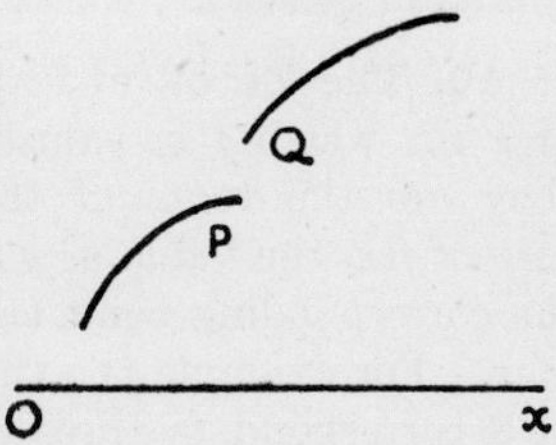

When the test in question is satisfied at each value of

x $(-\infty<x<\infty)$ we say that the function is continuous throughout, and so too is its graph. It will now be proved that this is always true of a real polynomial $f(x)$.

Consider first the monomial function $y = x^n$. Then $y+k = (x+h)^n$, so that

$$k = (x+h)^n - x^n = h(nx^{n-1} + n_{(2)}hx^{n-2} + \ldots + h^{n-1}) = hA,$$

where $n_{(2)} = n(n-1)/2!$, $n_{(r)} = n(n-1)\ldots(n-r+1)/r!$, a notation for the binomial coefficient. Each number x, h, n, $n_{(r)}$ is finite : the series has n terms and each term has a finite number of factors. Consequently A is finite. Hence k can be made as small as we please by taking h small enough. If k is to be made numerically less than ϵ we simply choose h numerically less than ϵ/B, where B is any non-zero constant which is numerically greater than the finite but variable A. Thus the function x^n is continuous throughout. Exactly similar remarks apply to $a_0 x^n$, to a sum of a finite number of such terms, and so to a polynomial in general.

10. The Zeros of f(x), f′(x) and f″(x). The values of x for which $f(x)$ vanishes are called the *zeros* of $f(x)$; they are the roots of the equation $f(x) = 0$. At each zero of $f(x)$ the value of y is zero ; hence if x is a real root the corresponding point (x, y) of the curve lies on the axis of x. For example the three points B, E, F of the figure in **8** correspond to three real roots of the cubic equation there represented, for which $x = -2$, 1 or 2.

From the differential calculus we know that $f'(x)$ gives the gradient of the tangent at (x, y) to the curve $y = f(x)$, and that $f'(x)$ vanishes at each point where the tangent is parallel to the axis of x. Such points are called *turning points*. At other points on the curve $f'(x)$ is either positive or negative. If positive, $f'(x)>0$, then at such points the curve is ascending, as x increases in value from left to right : if negative, $f'(x)<0$, the curve is descending as x increases.

Again, $f''(x)$ is positive whenever $f'(x)$ increases, that is, the gradient steepens, which always implies a bend of the curve with its concavity upwards ; and $f''(x)$ is negative whenever $f'(x)$ decreases, which happens when the bend of the curve has its concavity downwards. Each real zero of $f''(x)$ corresponds to a *point of inflexion* on the curve, whenever $f'''(x) \neq 0$. Such points separate the upward from the downward bends of the curve; these bends naturally must occur alternately. Usually the tangent at an inflexion is not parallel to the axis of x, but when it is, the point is both inflexion and turning point. The origin in the curve $y = x^3$ is a good example of such a point; and the reader should plot and draw the curve for inspection. Other turning points, for which $f'(x) = 0$, $f''(x) \neq 0$ are classified as maxima or minima points on the curve: the maxima are at the crests of the waves and the minima at the troughs.

Always reading from left to right (that is, with increasing x) we may sum up as follows:

The curve $y = f(x)$ rises	when	$f'(x) > 0$,
falls	,,	$f'(x) < 0$,
has a turning point	,,	$f'(x) = 0$,
a maximum	,,	$f'(x) = 0, f''(x) < 0$,
a minimum	,,	$f'(x) = 0, f''(x) > 0$,
is concave downwards	,,	$f''(x) < 0$,
is concave upwards	,,	$f''(x) > 0$,
has a point of inflexion	,,	$f''(x) = 0, f'''(x) \neq 0$.

1. Prove that the curve $y = x^3 - x^2 - 4x + 4$ of **8** has a maximum between C and D, an inflexion between D and E, and a minimum between E and F. (Maximum at $x = -0{\cdot}87$, inflexion at $x = +\frac{1}{3}$, and a minimum at $x = 1{\cdot}54$.)

2. The curve for which $f''(x) = 6x^2 + 3x + 1$ has no inflexions.

3. The curve $y = x^4 + x^3 + x^2 + ax + b$ has no inflexions: while $y = x^4 + x^3 - 9x^2 + ax + b$ has two inflexions.

4. Examine the case when both $f'(x) = 0, f''(x) = 0$.

11. Behaviour of a Polynomial at Infinity. It is useful to consider the behaviour of the polynomial $f(x)$

for large values of x, positive or negative. For this purpose let the function be provisionally written as

$$f(x) = a_0x^n \pm a_1x^{n-1} \pm a_2x^{n-2} \pm \ldots \pm a_n, \quad . \quad (1)$$

where the sign of each term is fixed, either + or −, and each of $a_1, a_2, \ldots, a_n$ is either positive or zero. If $x>0$ each power of x is positive, and the value of $f(x)$ obviously is not greater than

$$a_0x^n + a_1x^{n-1} + a_2x^{n-2} + \ldots + a_n \quad . \quad . \quad (2)$$

nor less than

$$a_0x^n - a_1x^{n-1} - a_2x^{n-2} - \ldots - a_n. \quad . \quad . \quad (3)$$

Also if $x>1$, then $x^n > x^{n-1} > x^{n-2} > \ldots > x > 1$. Hence a_rx^{n-r} is less than a_rx^{n-1} whenever $r = 2, 3, \ldots, n$. Consequently, if $x>1$,

$$a_0x^n + (a_1+a_2+\ldots+a_n)x^{n-1} > f(x) > a_0x^n - (a_1+a_2+\ldots a_n)x^{n-1}.$$

Hence, if $A = a_1+a_2+\ldots+a_n$, we have

$$(a_0+A/x)x^n > f(x) > (a_0-A/x)x^n. \quad . \quad . \quad (4)$$

Now choose a positive constant ϵ, however small. Since A is finite and positive, we can ensure that $A/x<\epsilon$ by taking $x>A/\epsilon$; that is, by taking x large enough we ensure that $f(x)$ lies between the values $y_1 = (a_0+\epsilon)x^n$ and $y_2 = (a_0-\epsilon)x^n$.

Geometrically, the graph of y must lie between those of y_1 and y_2 for large enough values of x. Let the graph of y_3 be drawn, where $y_3 = a_0x^n$, this being the limit of both y_1 and y_2 when $\epsilon \to 0$. The graphs y_1, y_2, y_3 then form two very acute curvilinear angles running from the origin and bending upwards into the first quadrant if $a_0>0$, and downwards into the fourth quadrant if $a_0<0$. Also y_1 is uppermost, y_2 lowest and y_3 between. For all large enough values of x the curve y is between the uppermost and the lowest of these boundaries—the shaded area of the figure. By changing ϵ to $\frac{1}{2}\epsilon$ or any such proper fraction of itself we decrease y_1, increase y_2 and leave y_3 unchanged. As $\epsilon \to 0$ the graph y approximates more and more closely to that of y_3, which acts as a curvilinear asymptote to y.

Analytically we say that for large values of x the function $f(x)$ behaves like a_0x^n, its leading term.

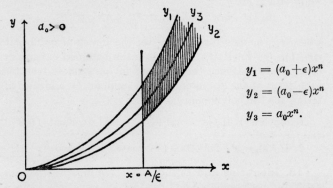

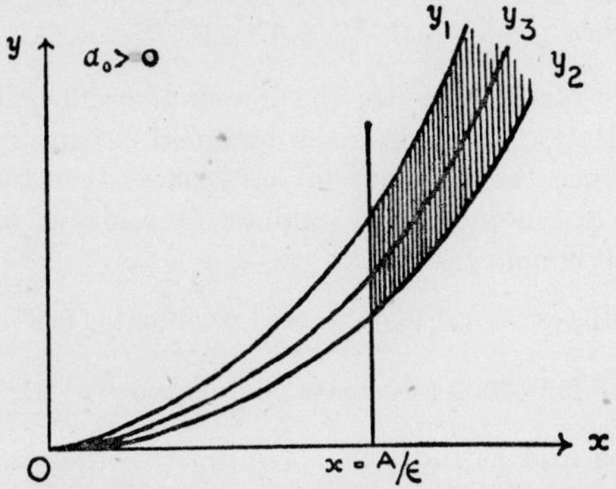

$$y_1 = (a_0+\epsilon)x^n$$
$$y_2 = (a_0-\epsilon)x^n$$
$$y_3 = a_0x^n.$$

Similarly, if x is negative and large, $f(x)$ behaves like a_0x^n. If n is odd, x negative and a_0 positive, then a_0x^n is negative, so that the curve is situated in the third quadrant. If n is even the curve is situated, for large negative values of x, in the second quadrant.

Example. $f(x) = x^3-x^2-4x+4.$

Here the sum of the absolute values of all coefficients except the first gives $A = 1+4+4 = 9$, so that $f(x)$ lies between $(1-\epsilon)x^3$ and $(1+\epsilon)x^3$ whenever $x > 9/\epsilon$ or $< -9/\epsilon$.

12. The Taylor Expansion of a Polynomial. A particular case of an important theorem based on repeated differentiation, first employed by James Gregory in 1670 but first published by Brook Taylor in 1715, is the following identity for a polynomial $f(x)$ of degree n:

$$f(x+h) = f(x)+hf'(x)+h^2f''(x)/2!+\ldots+h^nf^{(n)}(x)/n!, \quad (1)$$

where $f^{(r)}(x)$ denotes the rth derivative of $f(x)$.

Proof. The polynomial $f(x)$ is the sum of terms of type $a_r x^r$. Putting $f(x) = a_r x^r$ in the right-hand side of (1) and making use of

$$\frac{d^k}{dx^k} x^r = r(r-1)\ldots(r-k+1)x^{r-k},$$

we obtain

$$a_r \{x^r + hrx^{r-1} + h^2 r_{(2)} x^{r-2} + \ldots h^n r_{(n)} x^{r-n}\},$$

where $r_{(k)}$ denotes, as in **9**, p. 18, the binomial coefficient $r(r-1)\ldots(r-k+1)/k!$. But this is the binomial expansion of $a_r(x+h)^r$. Hence the theorem in question is true for each term of the polynomial $f(x)$; and so, by addition of terms, for the polynomial $f(x)$ itself.

Examples. 1. If $f(x) = ax^3 + 3bx^2 + 3cx + d$ evaluate $f(x+h)$ and $f(x-b/a)$.

2. If $f(x) = x^3 - 2x^2 + 3x - 4$ evaluate $f(x+2)$ and $f(x-1)$.

13. Identities and Equations. We must distinguish carefully between an identity and an equation. When a polynomial or other function $f(x)$ is thrown into another form $\phi(x)$ the relation $f(x) = \phi(x)$ is called an identity, as for example

$$2x^2 - 3x + 1 = (2x-1)(x-1).$$

An identity is characterized by the obvious property that when it is simplified to its basic terms they all vanish. Identities range from arithmetical cases, when no variable x appears, to highly elaborate cases involving many variables. It is also obvious that an identity is a relation which is true for every finite value of such variables. In the above instance, whatever finite value x has, the relation is true. But a much more important and converse fact holds, namely, that if

$$f(x) = a_0 x^n + a_1 x^{n-1} + \ldots + a_n = 0$$

is true for every finite value of x then $f(x) = 0$ is an identity.

First Proof. This proceeds by the use of determinants. Choose $n+1$ unequal numbers $\alpha, \beta, \ldots, \kappa$ and form the alternant

$$\Delta = |\alpha^n \beta^{n-1} \ldots \kappa^0|$$

in a notation where

$$|\alpha^1\beta^0| = \begin{vmatrix} \alpha & \beta \\ 1 & 1 \end{vmatrix}, \quad |\alpha^2\beta^1\gamma^0| = \begin{vmatrix} \alpha^2 & \beta^2 & \gamma^2 \\ \alpha & \beta & \gamma \\ 1 & 1 & 1 \end{vmatrix}$$

and so on. Then $f(\alpha) = a_0\alpha^n + \ldots + a_n = 0$, and we have $n+1$ homogeneous linear equations $f(\alpha) = 0$, $f(\beta) = 0$, ..., $f(\kappa) = 0$ for the $a_0, a_1, \ldots, a_n$ in terms of $\alpha, \beta, \ldots, \kappa$. By the theory of linear equations (Aitken, *Determinants and Matrices*, p. 64) *either* $\Delta = 0$ *or else* all the a_i vanish. But Δ is equal (*Ibid.*, p. 41) to the continued product of the $\frac{1}{2}n(n+1)$ differences of $\alpha, \beta, \ldots, \kappa$ taken in pairs, and so cannot vanish, since all of $\alpha, \beta, \ldots, \kappa$ differ. Hence all the a_i vanish, so that $f(x) = 0$ is an identity.

A corollary follows at once, that if $f(x)$ is a polynomial of degree n which vanishes for $n+1$ distinct values of x it vanishes identically for every value of x.

The argument given above is so important that it will be worth while to illustrate it for the case of the cubic $a_0x^3 + a_1x^2 + a_2x + a_3 = 0$.

If $\alpha, \beta, \gamma, \delta$ were four distinct roots then

$$\begin{aligned} a_0\alpha^3 + a_1\alpha^2 + a_2\alpha + a_3 &= 0 \\ a_0\beta^3 + a_1\beta^2 + a_2\beta + a_3 &= 0 \\ a_0\gamma^3 + a_1\gamma^2 + a_2\gamma + a_3 &= 0 \\ a_0\delta^3 + a_1\delta^2 + a_2\delta + a_3 &= 0. \end{aligned}$$

On eliminating a_0, a_1, a_2, a_3 from these equations we have

$$\Delta(\alpha\beta\gamma\delta) = \begin{vmatrix} \alpha^3 & \alpha^2 & \alpha & 1 \\ \beta^3 & \beta^2 & \beta & 1 \\ \gamma^3 & \gamma^2 & \gamma & 1 \\ \delta^3 & \delta^2 & \delta & 1 \end{vmatrix} = 0.$$

But $\Delta(\alpha\beta\gamma\delta) = (\alpha-\beta)(\alpha-\gamma)(\alpha-\delta)(\beta-\gamma)(\beta-\delta)(\gamma-\delta)$, and so, since $\Delta = 0$, two roots at least must be equal, contrary to hypothesis. It follows that the assumption is wrong, and that the cubic equation cannot have more than three distinct roots. In the same way an n-ic polynomial equation cannot have more than n distinct roots.

Second Proof. If $f(x) = 0$ for every value of x, $f(x)$ neither increases nor decreases in any range whatever, and so $f'(x) = 0$ for every value of x. But then, by the same reasoning, $f''(x) = 0$ for every value of x, and hence again $f'''(x) = 0$, and likewise all derivatives vanish. But since the Taylor series of $f(x)$ with respect to $x = 0$ is

$$f(x) = f(0)+xf'(0)+x^2f''(0)/2!+\ldots+x^nf^{(n)}(0)/n!,$$

we see that

$$a_n = f(0),\ a_{n-1} = f'(0),\ a_{n-2} = f''(0)/2!,\ \ldots,\ a_0 = f^{(n)}(0)/n!.$$

Hence all the a_i must be zero.

It follows from this theorem that if $f(x) = \phi(x)$ is an identity, true for every value of x, we may equate the coefficient of each power x^r on the left to that of x^r on the right. In fact we merely write $f(x)-\phi(x) = 0$ and apply the theorem. From an algebraic identity involving polynomials of the nth degree we thus obtain $n+1$ arithmetical identities. The identities so obtained may range from the most obvious tautologies to highly elaborate arithmetical propositions.

Unless all the a_i vanish $f(x) = 0$ is an equation of degree given by the index of the highest power of x whose coefficient does not vanish. Hence, by the above theorem, an equation of the nth degree cannot have more than n roots.

A polynomial identity can be described as having degree n when terms up to the power x^n occur in it. If so the identity must be taken at its face value—the description is given before simplification is undertaken. Thus

$$(x+1)(x-1)-x^2+1 = 0$$

is a quadratic identity. On the other hand,

$$(x+1)(x-1)-x^2+2x = 0$$

is not a quadratic but a linear equation.

14. The Practical Evaluation of a Polynomial. It is manifestly of importance to acquire facility in calculating the value of $f(x)$ for special values of x. How, for example, can we best evaluate $f(4)$ when $f(x) = 2x^3-3x^2+4x-5$? Instead of direct substitution, which is often troublesome and liable to errors, the following process, introduced in 1819 by Horner, is to be recommended, particularly as it furnishes the technique required also for the actual numerical solution of the equation $f(x) = 0$. The work is arranged as follows:

$$f(x) = 2x^3-3x^2+4x-5.$$

$$\begin{array}{rrrrl} 2 & -3 & +4 & -5\,(4 & \\ & 8 & 20 & 96 & \qquad f(4) = 91. \\ & \overline{5} & \overline{24} & \overline{91} & \end{array}$$

The coefficients 2, -3, 4, -5 with their proper signs are placed in a row according to descending powers of x. Missing powers must be indicated by zero coefficients. Thus we have four columns ($n+1$ in general). The argument 4 of the desired $f(4)$ is then entered, as if it were the quotient of a long division sum, beyond the final column. Beginning at the left the leading entry 2 is now multiplied by 4, the product, 8, being written below the next entry on the right and added. The result 5 is again multiplied by 4 and the product, 20, is added to the coefficient in the third column, giving 24. This again is multiplied by 4 and the product, 96, is added to the coefficient in the fourth, the last column. The process is then complete and the result is $f(4) = 91$.

The explanation is simple: and it is only necessary

to carry out the same procedure with letters to convince ourselves of its correctness :—

$$\begin{array}{ccccc} a & b & c & d & (x \\ & \underline{ax} & \underline{ax^2+bx} & \underline{ax^3+bx^2+cx} & \\ & ax+b & ax^2+bx+c & ax^3+bx^2+cx+d & = f(x). \end{array}$$

According to the rule the last entry in the final column, ax^3+bx^2+cx+d, should be the value of the polynomial whose coefficients in order are a, b, c, d and whose argument is x, and this is indeed the case. The method depends on the simple identity

$$f(x) = ((ax+b)x+c)x+d,$$

where brackets are introduced so as to resolve all powers of x into single factors. This can obviously be done for the general polynomial of degree n.

The reader will find it instructive to divide $2x^3-3x^2+4x-5$ by $x-4$, using long division. The quotient is $2x^2+5x+24$ and the remainder 91. Horner's method (sometimes called the method of synthetic division) provides all the materials for the quotient and remainder more compactly than the ordinary method : and it has the psychological advantage of employing addition rather than subtraction as the staple operation.

Horner's method yields the quotient and remainder at once whenever a polynomial $f(x)$ is divided by a linear divisor $x-\alpha$. For the more general divisor $\alpha x+\beta$, divide $f(x)$ first by α and then by $x+\beta/\alpha$. This yields the correct quotient, but the remainder R is relative to $x+\beta/\alpha$. It must be remultiplied by α to give the correct remainder.

The method does not apply to quadratic and higher divisors.

Examples. If $f(x) = x^5-2x^4+3$, find $f(-3)$.

$$\begin{array}{rrrrrrl} 1 & -2 & 0 & 0 & 0 & 3 & (-3 \\ & \underline{-3} & \underline{15} & \underline{-45} & \underline{135} & \underline{-405} & \\ & -5 & 15 & -45 & 135 & -402 & = f(-3). \end{array}$$

Find also $f(4)$, $f(0{\cdot}2)$, $f(3)$, and try other values of x.

15. The Graphical Method of Lill. An interesting graphical method of evaluating $f(a)$, devised by Lill, has an advantage when the coefficients of the polynomial are awkward decimals, but an approximate result alone is required. Squared paper is useful.

We lay off straight lines AB, BC, CD, DE, ... of lengths equal to the respective coefficients a_0, a_1, a_2, a_3, ... At each point B, C, D, ... there is a right angle corner between consecutive lines, to the right if the next coefficient has the same sign and to the left if the sign changes. The whole track ABCDE... may be regarded as a plan of a route through a rectangular system of streets. We shall suppose that none of the coefficients vanish, so that there are $n+1$ segments and n corners to the route. Such a graph is clearly a representation of the function, a new type but none the less a representation.

Now take an acute angle θ, such that $\tan \theta = x$: then one such angle corresponds to a given real x, positive or negative, and the sign of θ is the same as that of x. Draw a line AP meeting BC (produced if necessary) at P, and such that the angle BAP is θ. If AB is set off horizontally from left to right, then P falls below AB when x is negative and above when x is positive. Draw a broken line APQR... such that the angles P, Q, ... are right angles situated on the lines BC, CD, DE, ... respectively. Then the value of $f(x)$ is given by the distance RE, from the last such point R to E, the end of the final segment a_n. This distance is measured according to the sense of the distance DE : thus in the first illustration DE is $+4$, the direction of measurement is from D to E, hence RE is positive. In the second illustration DE is -3, therefore RE, having the same sign as DE, is negative.

To prove the result we work out the segments step by step. Thus in the first figure $AB = a_0$, $BP = a_0 \tan \theta$, $PC = a_1 + a_0 \tan \theta = a_0 x + a_1$. But $QC = PC \tan \theta$, hence

$$QD = CD - CQ = a_2 + (a_1 + a_0 x)x.$$

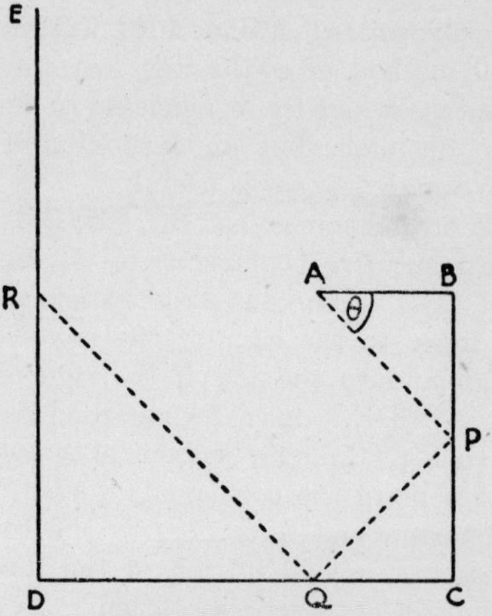

$x^3+2x^2+3x+4.$

No change of sign : all corners to the right.

($\theta = -45°$, $x = -1$). Compare Ex. 8, p. 33.

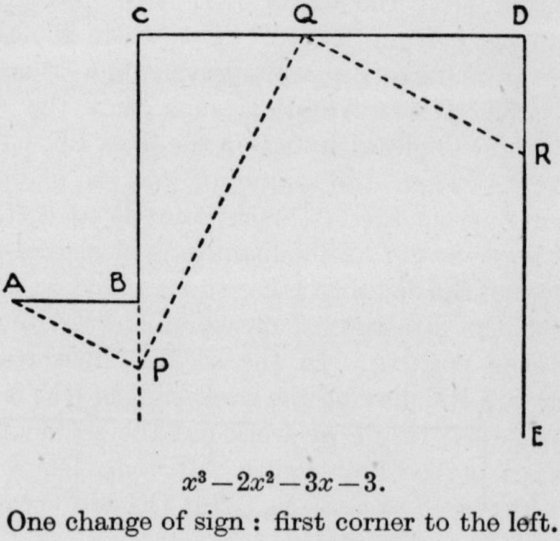

$x^3-2x^2-3x-3.$

One change of sign : first corner to the left.

($\theta<0$, $\tan\theta = x = -\frac{1}{2}$).

Finally, $\quad RE = DE - DR = DE - DQ \tan\theta$
$$= a_3 + QD\, x$$
$$= a_0x^3 + a_1x^2 + a_2x + a_3.$$

The process can be applied to all such cases and for all values of n.

Evidently the equation is solved whenever the point R coincides with E, for in this case RE vanishes. It requires but little practice to see that this would happen, in our first illustrative example, when θ is rather more than 45°. This furnishes an interesting and ingenious method for locating the roots of an equation.

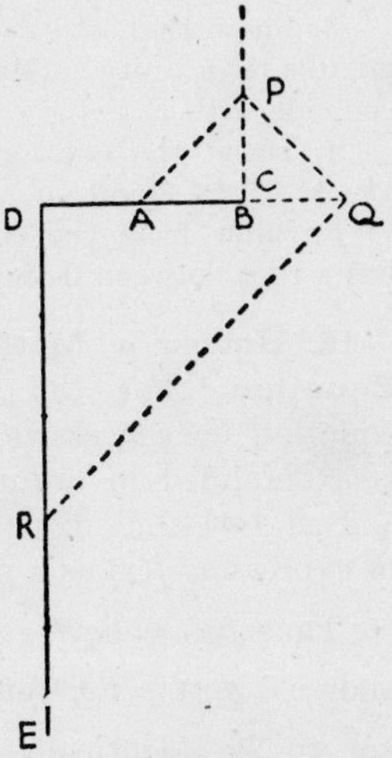

$x^3+2x-5.$

Examples. 1. Adapt the rule to the case where one or more of the intermediate coefficients are lacking.

Proceed as before but make the necessary points coincide. For x^3+2x-5 we have AB = 1, CD = 2, DE = 5. Whether BC is regarded as +0 or −0

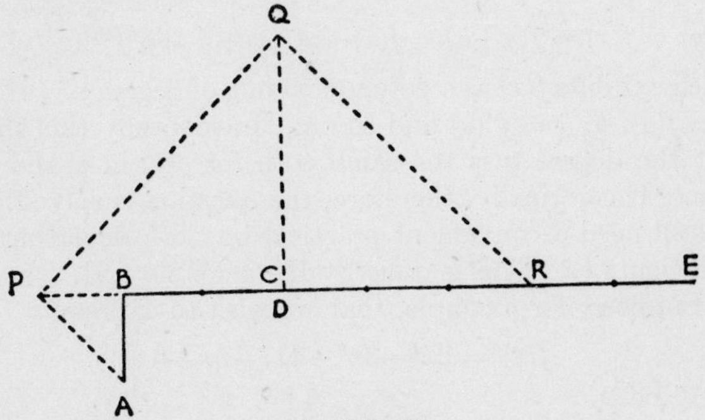

$x^3+2x^2-5.$

the rule requires CD to be in BA produced, a right-about or a left-about turn.

2. Justify the preceding figures for x^3+2x-5 and for x^3+2x^2-5, where $f(x)$ is represented by RE with $x = 1$.

3. Show that $x^3+2x-5 = 0$ has a root which is slightly greater than unity. (Move P slightly upwards to cause R to coincide with E.)

4. Draw the zigzag graphs ABC... for x^2-4, x^3+8, $x^4+x^3+2x^2+2x+1$.

5. Show from the zigzag that $2x^4-2x^3+4x^2-4x+1 = 0$ has a root between 0 and 1.

16. Horner's Method of Reducing an Algebraic Equation. For the purpose of solving a numerical equation by successive approximations—a method which is exemplified in ordinary arithmetic when we calculate $\sqrt{2}$ as 1·4142..., digit by digit—we need a practical way of expressing $f(x)$ as a polynomial $g(y)$ where $y = x+a$.

Thus $f(x) = a_0x^n+a_1x^{n-1}+\ldots+a_{n-1}x+a_n$ . . (1)

and $g(y) = b_0y^n+b_1y^{n-1}+\ldots+b_{n-1}y+b_n$ . . (2)

are to be identically equal when $y = x-a$. The coefficients a_i are supposed known; so too is a. We require to find the coefficients b_i.

This can of course be done by Taylor's theorem; in fact

$$g(y) = f(x) = f(y+a) = f(a)+yf'(a)+\ldots+y^nf^{(n)}(a)/n!, \quad (3)$$

which exhibits $f(x)$ as a polynomial in y of degree n. Hence $b_n = f(a)$, $b_{n-1} = f'(a)$ and so on. Incidentally this shows that the degree n is the same both for $g(y)$ in y and $f(x)$ in x. Theoretically, therefore, the question is solved, but we still need a convenient practical way of calculating the coefficients b_i. This is done by Horner's method.

Suppose, for example, that we wish to express

$$f(x) = 2x^4-3x^3+4x^2-5x+6$$

in the form

$$b_0(x-2)^4+b_1(x-2)^3+b_2(x-2)^2+b_3(x-2)+b_4.$$

We apply Horner's method, dividing $f(x)$ by $x-2$. From the Horner scheme

$$\begin{array}{ccccc} 2 & -3 & 4 & -5 & 6\ (2 \\ & 4 & 2 & 12 & 14 \\ \hline & 1 & 6 & 7 & 20 \end{array}$$

we infer that the quotient is $2x^3+x^2+6x+7$ and that the remainder is 20. In fact

$$2x^4-3x^3+4x^2-5x+6 = (2x^3+x^2+6x+7)(x-2)+20.$$

The reader will find it instructive to reverse the process and start by multiplying out this identity. The above scheme will then be seen from another point of view.

Now let $2x^3+x^2+6x+7$ be treated similarly and divided by $x-2$. From the scheme

$$\begin{array}{cccc} 2 & 1 & 6 & 7\ (2 \\ & 4 & 10 & 32 \\ \hline & 5 & 16 & 39 \end{array}$$

we infer that $2x^3+x^2+6x+7 = (2x^2+5x+16)(x-2)+39$. Again, from

$$\begin{array}{ccc} 2 & 5 & 16\ (2 \\ & 4 & 18 \\ \hline & 9 & 34 \end{array}$$

we infer that $2x^2+5x+16 = (2x+9)(x-2)+34$, and finally from

$$\begin{array}{cc} 2 & 9\ (2 \\ & 4 \\ \hline & 13 \end{array}$$

that $$2x+9 = 2(x-2)+13.$$

We can telescope these results and write

$$\begin{aligned} 2x^4-3x^3+4x^2-5x+6 &= (((2y+13)y+34)y+39)y+20 \\ &= 2y^4+13y^3+34y^2+39y+20, \end{aligned}$$

where $y = x-2$, and this is the required form. In fact

$$b_0 = 2,\ b_1 = 13,\ b_2 = 34,\ b_3 = 39,\ b_4 = 20.$$

We notice that the successive remainders have furnished the coefficients b from right to left, except for b_0, which is the same as a_0. Clearly too the process is true in general: the b_i are the remainders on dividing by y $(= x-a)$ first $f(x)$ and then its successive quotients.

Furthermore—and this is the chief advantage of the method—we can tabulate the whole process in one scheme:

2	−3	4	−5	6 (2
	4	2	12	14
	1	6	7	20
	4	10	32	
	5	16	39	
	4	18		
	9	34		
	4			
	13			

$$f(x) = 2x^4-3x^3+4x^2-5x+6$$
$$= 2y^4+13y^3+34y^2+39y+20,$$
where $y = x-2$.

It will be seen that this scheme incorporates all that has been said, but without needless repetition. The method is easy to memorize directly from such a scheme. Build the scheme from left to right by rows. At each step multiply the balance in a column by $a (a = 2$ above) and add it to the balance in the next column to the right. Perform the step once in the last column, twice in the last but one, and so on. Rule off with a vertical line at the completion of each stage.

Examples. 1.

1	4	0	−70 (3
	3	21	63
	7	21	−7
	3	30	
	10	51	
	3		
	13		

$$f(x) = x^3+4x^2-70$$
$$= y^3+13y^2+51y-7,$$
where $y = x-3$.

2. Prove by Horner's method that

$$x^4-1 = (x+1)^4-4(x+1)^3+6(x+1)^2-4(x+1).$$

3. Express $f(x)$ as a polynomial in y when

$f(x) = x^3-4x^2+70$ and $y = x-3$; also when $y = x+3$.

4. From Example 1 obtain $f'(3), f''(3), f'''(3)$. (51, 26, 6).

5. Evaluate $(2x^5-3x^4+5x^2-6x+7) \div (x-2), \div (x+2)$, and again $\div (x+3)$.

6. Obtain a, b, c, d, e, f from the identity

$$x^6+x^3+1 = (x-2)^6+a(x-2)^5+b(x-2)^4 \\ +c(x-2)^3+d(x-2)^2+e(x-2)+f.$$

7. If $x^3-4x^2+8x-1 =$

$$(x-1)(x-2)(x-3)+a(x-1)(x-2)+b(x-1)+c,$$

find a, b, c.

1	−4	8	−1 (1, 2, 3
	1	−3	5
	−3	5	4 = c
	2	−2	
	−1	3 = b	
	3		
	2 = a		

8. 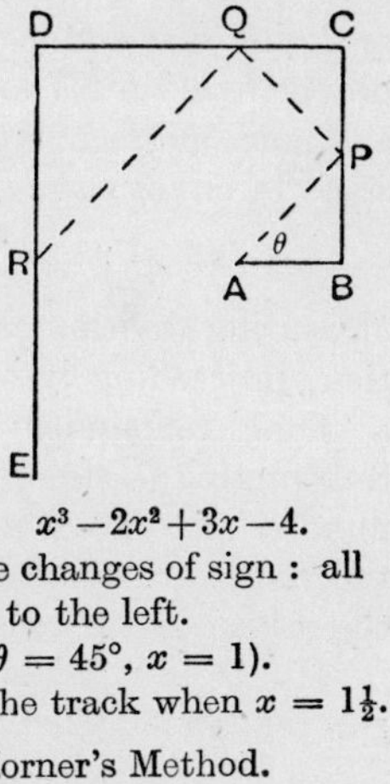

x^3-2x^2+3x-4.

Three changes of sign : all corners to the left.

($\theta = 45°$, $x = 1$).

Draw the track when $x = 1\frac{1}{2}$.

9. Reduce £4, 2s. 8d. to pence by Horner's Method.

4	2	8
	80	984
	82	992

Thus Horner's Method is simply the systematic use of a very familiar process in elementary arithmetic.

CHAPTER III

THE THEORY OF RATIONAL FUNCTIONS

17. The Division of Polynomials. The arithmetical process of division plays two distinct rôles: it is either a *sharing*, or else a *measuring*, process. To divide 28 inches into 7 equal parts is a sharing process, to find out how many times a length 7 inches is contained in 28 inches is a measuring process, but the same arithmetical symbol $28 \div 7$ is used for both. When the exact multiple 28 of 7 is replaced by a number such as 23, which is not a multiple of 7, the distinction is more evident: sharing leads to a proper fraction 2/7 as remainder, while measuring leads to a whole number remainder 2. The quotient 3 is the same in either case.

$$23 \div 7; \quad 23/7 = 3+2/7, \quad 23 = 3 \times 7+2.$$

Measuring division may be regarded as repeated subtraction, proceeding just so far as to produce a zero, or else a final remainder which is less than the divisor. Subtracting 7 step by step, we have 23, 16, 9, 2. The number of terms which are not less than the divisor gives the quotient, while the term, if any, which is less than the divisor is the remainder.

If D = dividend, d = divisor, q = quotient, r = remainder, then we can state these facts in the form

$$D \div d; \; D/d = q+r/d, \; D = qd+r.$$

When D and d are positive integers, so also are q and r, with the important condition that $0 \leqslant r < d$.

In algebra these statements are closely paralleled by the properties of polynomial division. A whole number such as 384 is really a quadratic polynomial in respect to ten: $384 = 3x^2+8x+4$, when $x = 10$. A decimal terminating fraction such as 384·25 is really a rational function of ten, expressed as partial fractions,

$$384{\cdot}25 = 3x^2+8x+4+\frac{2}{x}+\frac{5}{x^2} \text{ when } x = 10.$$

A non-terminating decimal is an infinite series in descending powers of ten. Thus the polynomial $f(x)$ in algebra plays the part of the whole number in arithmetic, while the rational function

$$R(x) = f(x)/\phi(x)$$

composed of two polynomials, whose degrees are m and n respectively, plays the part of the arithmetical fraction.

Let $f(x) = a_0x^m+a_1x^{m-1}+\ldots+a_{m-1}x+a_m, \quad a_0\neq 0,$

$\phi(x) = c_0x^n+c_1x^{n-1}+\ldots+c_{n-1}x+c_n, \quad c_0\neq 0,$

where all the coefficients a_i and c_i are constants. If $m\geqslant n$ the function $R(x)$ is called an *improper*, and if $m<n$ a *proper*, fraction with regard to x. If $m\geqslant n$ we may divide $f(x)$ by $\phi(x)$ and obtain

$$f(x)/\phi(x) = q(x)+r(x)/\phi(x), \quad f(x) = q(x)\phi(x)+r(x),$$

where $q(x)$ is a polynomial of degree $m-n$, and $r(x)$ is one of degree less than n. For example

$$\frac{x^4+2x^3-x+1}{x^3-2x+3} = (x+2)+\frac{2x^2-5}{x^3-2x+3},$$

$$x^4+2x^3-x+1 = (x+2)(x^3-2x+3)+(2x^2-5).$$

Let us note the following properties: (i) $R(x)$ reduces to a polynomial when n is zero, or else when $\phi(x)$ is a factor of $f(x)$, in which case $r(x)$ vanishes identically.

(ii) The highest term in $q(x)$ is $a_0c_0^{-1}x^{m-n}$, as is seen by actual division, so that the degree of $q(x)$ is $m-n$.

(iii) The relation $f(x) = q(x)\phi(x)+r(x)$ is identically true for every value of x.

This division process is unique; for if not, let q_1 and r_1 be another quotient and remainder of $f \div \phi$, so that

$$f(x) = q\phi + r = q_1\phi + r_1,$$

where, for brevity, q is written instead of $q(x)$, and so on. Then $(q-q_1)\phi = r-r_1$ identically. If $q \neq q_1$ the left-hand expression is a polynomial expression of degree at least that of ϕ, whereas the degree of both r and r_1 and therefore of their difference is less than that of ϕ. This (*cf.* p. 24) is impossible: hence $q = q_1$, so that $r = r_1$, and the division is unique.

By Euclid's method of repeated measuring, commonly called the G.C.M. or the H.C.F. process, we can discover whether $f(x)$ and $\phi(x)$ possess a polynomial factor in common. Again, for brevity, let single letters denote polynomials. Divide f by ϕ giving remainder r: divide ϕ by r giving a remainder r_1: divide r by r_1 giving a remainder r_2, and so on. Thus

$$\begin{aligned} f &= q\phi + r, \\ \phi &= q_1 r + r_1, \\ r &= q_2 r_1 + r_2, \\ &\cdots\cdots\cdots \\ r_{p-2} &= q_p r_{p-1} + r_p. \end{aligned}$$

Each of f, ϕ, r, r_1, ... is a polynomial, where the degree of r is less than that of ϕ, that of r_1 is less than that of r, and so on. Consequently the process must terminate since the degree of ϕ is finite. *Either* a remainder r_p vanishes identically, *or* the degree of the last r_p is zero, that is, r_p is a constant $c \neq 0$.

Case 1. If $r_p = 0$ and all its predecessors are non-zero, then r_{p-1} is a factor of r_{p-2}. But $r_{p-3} = q_{p-1}r_{p-2} + r_{p-1}$, so that r_{p-1} is also a factor of r_{p-3}, and so on throughout all the equations. Thus r_{p-1} is a factor common to f, ϕ and to each r.

Conversely, any factor s common to f and ϕ is a factor of $f-q\phi$ and therefore of r, similarly of $\phi-q_1r$, that is of r_1, and so on. Hence r_{p-1} includes *every* common factor of f and ϕ: it must therefore be the highest common factor (H.C.F.) or greatest common measure (G.C.M.) of f and ϕ.

Case 2. If the last remainder is c, a non-zero constant, it must include as before every common factor of f and ϕ. Since c is free from x we say that, in this case, f and ϕ are polynomials which are prime to each other. They have no common factor.

Hence any two polynomials are either prime to each other or else have a common polynomial factor. The above Euclidean process is unique and rational; and it will inevitably detect any factor common to f and ϕ. We denote the G.C.M. by G, and in Case 2 we take $G = 1$.

Theorem 1. Each partial remainder r, including G, can be expressed in the form $Af+B\phi$, where A and B are polynomials of degree less than ϕ and f respectively.

Proof. Solving the relation for $r, r_1, r_2, \ldots$ in succession, we obtain

$$\begin{aligned} r &= f-q\phi &&= A_0f+B_0\phi, \text{ say,} \\ r_1 &= -q_1f+(qq_1+1)\phi &&= A_1f+B_1\phi, \\ r_2 &= (q_1q_2+1)f-(qq_1q_2+q+q_2)\phi &&= A_2f+B_2\phi, \end{aligned}$$

and so on. In this way the row r_k is obtained on multiplying the preceding row by $-q_k$ and adding the last but one row. Hence each partial remainder is expressed in the form $Af+B\phi$, where A and B are polynomials.

Again, by the mode of formation, A_k the coefficient of f contains as highest term $\pm q_1q_2\ldots q_k$, while that of B_k is $\pm qq_1q_2\ldots q_k$. Now from (1) the degree of f is that of $q\phi$, the degree of ϕ is that of q_1r: indeed the continued products

$$f\phi r\ldots r_{p-2}, \quad q\phi q_1rq_2r_1\ldots q_pr_{p-1}$$

have the same degree. Remove the common factors: therefore f and $qq_1q_2\ldots q_pr_{p-1}$ have the same degree. But r_{p-1}, being a remainder before the last, must involve x

and have a positive degree, so that the degree of $qq_1 \ldots q_p$ is *less* than that of f.

Once more, on applying the same argument to all but the first equation of (1), the degree of $q_1 q_2 \ldots q_p$ is less than that of ϕ.

Accordingly the degree of every A is less than that of ϕ, and of every B is less than that of f.

Corollary. Polynomials A and B exist for any pair of polynomials f and ϕ, such that either $Af+B\phi = G$ or $Af+B\phi = 1$, where G is the G.C.M. of f and ϕ, or else f and ϕ are prime to each other.

The corollary is proved by applying the above theorem to the final non-zero remainder, which is either G or a constant c. In the latter case divide $Af+B\phi = c$ throughout by c and rename the polynomial coefficients of f and ϕ, as A and B.

This theorem, with its corollary, is of fundamental importance in many branches of algebra.

Examples. 1. $f = x^3+1$, $\phi = x^2+1$. Here the successive division processes give

$$x^3+1 = x(x^2+1)+(-x+1) \text{ where } q = x,\ r = -x+1,$$
$$x^2+1 = (-x+1)(-x-1)+2, \quad q_1 = -x-1,\ r_1 = 2.$$

Hence f and ϕ are prime to each other. Also

$$x^2+1 = [x^3+1-x(x^2+1)](-x-1)+2.$$

Thus $(x+1)(x^3+1)+(1-x-x^2)(x^2+1) = 2$, so that $A(= \frac{1}{2}(x+1))$ is of degree less than that of ϕ, and $B(= \frac{1}{2}(1-x-x^2))$ is of degree less than that of f.

2. $f = x^3+1$, $\phi = x^2-1$. Here $x^3+1 = x(x^2-1)+x+1$, $x^2-1 = (x-1)(x+1)$. Thus $G = x+1$, and $(x^3+1)-x(x^2-1) = x+1$ shows that $A = 1$, $B = -x$, where $Af+B\phi = G$.

18. Reduction to Lowest Terms. A proper fraction $p(x)/q(x)$ cannot be identically equal to a polynomial $f(x)$; otherwise $p(x) = f(x)q(x)$ would be an identity, where at least one term on the left is of higher degree than any on the right and therefore (*cf.* p. 24) could not cancel out.

The combination, in sum or difference, of a finite number of algebraic proper fractions always gives a proper fraction : for

$$\frac{p}{q}+\frac{r}{s}=\frac{ps+qr}{qs} \quad . \quad . \quad . \quad (1)$$

and the degrees of both ps and qr are less than the degree of qs when p/q and r/s are proper fractions. For n such terms, add them one by one, applying this argument each time.

In individual arithmetical cases this property is not necessarily true.

Example. $\frac{x^2}{x^3+1}+\frac{x}{x^2+1}$ gives a single fraction whose degree is four in the numerator and five in the denominator. Put $x = 1$; the sum is not a proper fraction.

Theorem 2. If f is prime to ϕ then f/ϕ cannot be reduced to terms of lower degree.

Proof. If possible let $f/\phi = f_1/\phi_1$, where f_1 is prime to ϕ_1. Divide f by ϕ, and f_1 by ϕ_1: let the respective remainders be r, r_1. Then

$$\frac{q\phi+r}{\phi}=\frac{q_1\phi_1+r_1}{\phi_1}$$

or
$$q-q_1=\frac{r}{\phi}-\frac{r_1}{\phi_1},$$

where $q-q_1$ is a polynomial and the right-hand expression is a proper fraction. Hence both vanish, so that $r/\phi = r_1/\phi_1$. Hence

$$f/f_1 = \phi/\phi_1 = r/r_1 = \ldots .$$

This process has reduced ϕ/ϕ_1 to a fraction r/r_1 of lower degree in both numerator and denominator. Let it therefore be repeated until, say, r_k/r_{k+1} is reached, where either r_k or r_{k+1} is a constant which may be taken as unity. If r_{k+1} is a constant and r_k is not, then $f = f_1r_k$, $\phi = \phi_1r_k$ shows f and ϕ both factorized, whereas by hypothesis f

was prime to ϕ. Similarly, r_k cannot be a constant while r_{k+1} is not; so that both are constant, and so too is $r_k/r_{k+1} = \lambda$, say. Thus $f = \lambda f_1$, $\phi = \lambda\phi_1$ and f/ϕ can differ from f_1/ϕ_1 by a constant factor only in numerator and denominator. Thus f/ϕ cannot be reduced to terms of lower degree.

Theorem 3. The form $Af+B\phi = G$ or 1 is unique, where A and B are lower in degree than ϕ/G and f/G respectively.

Proof. If f and ϕ have a common factor, write $f = Gf_1$, $\phi = G\phi_1$ and treat the prime case $Af_1+B\phi_1 = 1$.

Assume now that f is prime to ϕ, and that a second such identity $Cf+D\phi = 1$ exists. By division express C as $Q\phi+A_0$ and D as $Pf+B_0$, where A_0 is of degree less than that of ϕ and B_0 less than that of f. Hence

$$(A_0+Q\phi)f+(B_0+Pf)\phi = 1. \quad . \quad . \quad (2)$$

This is an identity, where $f\phi$ is of degree $m+n$, A_0f is of lower degree, and so is $B_0\phi$. Unless $P+Q = 0$, the identity contains terms $(P+Q)f\phi$ of degree at least $m+n$ which cannot vanish. This is impossible (*cf.* p. 24). Hence $P+Q = 0$ and $A_0f+B_0\phi = 1$.

Once more, A_0 and B_0 must be the A and B of the Theorem 1; for if not we have $A_0f+B_0\phi=1=Af+B\phi$, so that $(A_0-A)f = (B-B_0)\phi$. Unless $A = A_0$, $B = B_0$ this reduces the fraction f/ϕ to lower terms $(B-B_0)/(A_0-A)$, which is impossible when f is prime to ϕ: thus $A = A_0$, $B = B_0$ and the formula $Af+B\phi = 1$ is unique.

19. Partial Fractions. Let $\phi(x)$ be capable of breaking up into two polynomial factors ϕ_1, ϕ_2 which are prime to each other. Then, by the Theorem 1, we can find polynomials (or constants) A_1 and A_2, of lower degrees than ϕ_1 and ϕ_2 respectively, such that $A_2\phi_1+A_1\phi_2 = 1$. This at once enables us to resolve $f(x)/\phi(x)$ into partial fractions; for

$$\frac{f(x)}{\phi(x)} = \frac{f(x)(A_2\phi_1+A_1\phi_2)}{\phi_1\phi_2} = \frac{A_1f}{\phi_1} + \frac{A_2f}{\phi_2}. \quad . \quad (1)$$

On performing the division, if improper fractions occur in either of the pair, we obtain

$$\frac{f(x)}{\phi(x)} = q(x) + \frac{r_1(x)}{\phi_1(x)} + \frac{r_2(x)}{\phi_2(x)}, \qquad . \quad . \quad (2)$$

where $q(x)$ is the total quotient, and r_1, r_2 are the respective remainders, for the divisors ϕ_1 and ϕ_2.

Example. $$\frac{2x^4}{(x^2+1)(x+1)} = 2x-2-\frac{x-1}{x^2+1}+\frac{1}{x+1}.$$

The reader will be familiar with simple examples of the method of partial fractions. Certain observations can therefore be shortly stated: (i) any common factors of f and ϕ are first removed before resolution into partial fractions is attempted: (ii) the quotient $q(x)$ is of degree $m-n$ and only appears if m, the degree of f, is not less than n, that of ϕ: (iii) ϕ_1 and ϕ_2 must have no common factor, although each can be of any degree: (iv) if ϕ_1 is of degree p the numerator $r_1(x)$ is a polynomial of degree less than p.

If either ϕ_1 or ϕ_2 has polynomial factors the process may be repeated, until all the distinct factors of ϕ are segregated. Thus we express the rational function $R(x)$ as a sum of partial fractions in the form

$$R(x) = \frac{f(x)}{\phi(x)} = q(x) + \Sigma\frac{r(x)}{\psi(x)}, \qquad . \quad . \quad (3)$$

where no two of the denominators $\psi(x)$ have any factor in common, and each $r(x)$ is of lower degree than its denominator.

Various cases arise:

(i) The simple case, when $\phi(x) = (x-\alpha)(x-\beta)\ldots(x-\lambda)$ is a product of n distinct linear factors in which $\alpha, \beta, \ldots, \lambda$ all differ. We write $\phi(x) = \Pi(x-\alpha)$.

(ii) The repeated factor case, when

$$\phi(x) = (x-\alpha)^r(x-\beta)^s\ldots,$$

where α, β, ... all differ but one or more of r, s, ... exceeds unity. We write $\phi(x) = \Pi(x-\alpha)^r$.

(iii) The simple quadratic case, when $\phi(x)$ has quadratic factors x^2+px+q, with or without linear factors, and $p^2<4q$.

(iv) The repeated quadratic case.

In any case the polynomial quotient $q(x)$ must be evaluated by an ordinary division process. In the simple case, (i), each partial fraction will take the form $a/(x-\alpha)$, where the denominator is linear and the numerator, being of lower degree, is necessarily a constant only. Hence we have an identity

$$\frac{f(x)}{\phi(x)} = q(x)+\Sigma\,\frac{a}{x-\alpha}.$$

To evaluate a, multiply throughout by $x-\alpha$. Every term on the right will then contain $x-\alpha$ as a factor except the term a itself. Put $x=\alpha$ and the right-hand member is a alone. On the left we shall have

$$f(\alpha)/\{(\alpha-\beta)(\alpha-\gamma)...(\alpha-\lambda)\},$$

which must therefore be equal to a. Similarly for each numerator of the partial fractions.

Examples. 1. $\dfrac{x^3}{x^2-3x+2} = x+3+\dfrac{a}{x-1}+\dfrac{b}{x-2}.$

Here $x^2-3x+2 = (x-1)(x-2)$ and $q(x) = x+3$ by division. Multiply through by $x-1$ and then put $x = 1$. Thus $\dfrac{1}{1-2} = a$. Similarly, $\dfrac{8}{2-1} = b$, so that $a = -1$, $b = 8$.

2. If $\phi(x) = (x-\alpha)(x-\beta)(x-\gamma)$ where α, β, γ differ, prove that

$$\frac{\phi'(x)}{\phi(x)} = \frac{1}{x-\alpha}+\frac{1}{x-\beta}+\frac{1}{x-\gamma}.$$

3. $\dfrac{f(x)}{\phi(x)} = q(x)+\dfrac{f(\alpha)}{(x-\alpha)\phi'(\alpha)}+...+\dfrac{f(\lambda)}{(x-\lambda)\phi'(\lambda)}$

where $\phi(x) = (x-\alpha)(x-\beta)...(x-\lambda)$. If $f(x)$ is of lower degree than $\phi(x)$, the quotient $q(x)$ vanishes.

To prove this, observe that $\phi'(x) = (x-\beta)(x-\gamma)...(x-\lambda)$ plus terms all involving $x-\alpha$ as a factor. Hence $\phi'(\alpha) = (\alpha-\beta)(\alpha-\gamma)...(\alpha-\lambda)$. Hence the value of a in the partial fraction $a/(x-\alpha)$ is $f(\alpha)/\phi'(\alpha)$, and the result follows.

4. If $f(x)$ is a cubic polynomial and α, β, γ, δ are any four distinct numbers, show that

$$f(x) = \Sigma f(\alpha) \frac{(x-\beta)(x-\gamma)(x-\delta)}{(\alpha-\beta)(\alpha-\gamma)(\alpha-\delta)}$$

summed for the four terms due to the distinct combinations $\beta\gamma\delta$, $\gamma\delta\alpha$, $\delta\alpha\beta$, $\alpha\beta\gamma$.

This follows from Example 3. It is Lagrange's interpolation formula for a cubic polynomial, and it applies in general, with the necessary changes, to the n-ic.

Case (ii). If $\phi(x) = (x-\alpha)^r(x-\beta)^s$ ... the general rule gives

$$\frac{f(x)}{\phi(x)} = q(x)+\Sigma \frac{A}{(x-\alpha)^r}$$

where A is a polynomial of degree less than r.

Put $x-\alpha = y$ and express A by Horner's method as a polynomial $p_1+p_2y+p_3y^2+...$ of degree less than r. The partial fraction due to $x-\alpha$ is then $(p_1+p_2y+...)/y^r$, which separates at once into the terms

$$\frac{p_1}{(x-\alpha)^r}+\frac{p_2}{(x-\alpha)^{r-1}}+...+\frac{p_r}{x-\alpha},$$

where the numerators are constants. At most there are n such partial fractions: in particular cases some, after the first, may vanish. Similarly, here are at most s terms due to β, and so on.

In practice the calculation of the numerators is troublesome whenever $r>2$; but p_1 is obtained at once on multiplying throughout by $(x-\alpha)^r$ and then putting $x = \alpha$. If $r = 2$, multiply throughout by $(x-\alpha)^r$, differentiate with respect to x and then put $x = \alpha$. This gives p_2. In higher cases multiplication and further differentiation yield the successive numerators of the partial fractions in question, but probably Horner's method is more rapid than this. In some cases equating of coefficients gives the results quite rapidly.

Examples. 1.

$$\frac{x^3}{(x+2)^2(x^2-1)} = \frac{p}{(x+2)^2}+\frac{q}{x+2}+\frac{r}{x-1}+\frac{s}{x+1}.$$

Hence $$\frac{x^3}{x^2-1} = p+(x+2)q+(x+2)^2[\ldots].$$

First put $x = -2$; then $-8/3 = p$. Next differentiate: the third term on the right then becomes

$$2(x+2)[\ldots]+(x+2)^2[\ldots]',$$

where the brackets indicate fractions with $x\pm 1$ in the denominators to first or second powers. On putting $x = -2$ these denominators do not vanish. Hence the third term $(x+2)^2[\ldots]$ vanishes after differentiation without the need for calculating explicitly the expression in the bracket. Thus

$$\frac{3x^2}{x^2-1}-\frac{x^3\,.\,2x}{(x^2-1)^2} = q+(x+2)\{\ldots\},$$

giving $q = 4/9$. Also $r = 1/18$, $s = \frac{1}{2}$.

Alternatively, we might form relations between the unknown coefficients by substituting other special values of x. Here $x = 0$ gives $\frac{1}{4}p+\frac{1}{2}q-r+s = 0$, so that when the values of p, r and s are found as before we obtain $q = 4/9$.

2. $$\frac{x^3}{(x+2)^4(x^2-1)} = \frac{A}{(x+2)^4}+\frac{1}{162(x-1)}+\frac{1}{2(x+1)},$$

where A is a cubic in x and the other fractions have been evaluated by the ordinary method. Put $x+2 = y$, $A = p_1+p_2y+p_3y^2+p_4y^3$, and multiply throughout by the denominator involving x. Thus

$$(y-2)^3=[p_1+p_2y+p_3y^2+p_4y^3](y^2-4y+3)+y^4\left[\frac{y-1}{162}+\frac{y-3}{2}\right].$$

Now pick out coefficients of y. We find $p_1 = -8/3$, $p_2 = 4/9$, $p_3 = -14/27$, $p_4 = -41/81$ most easily from the coefficients of y^0, y^1, y^4, y^5, and can use y^2, y^3 for checking the result.

Case (iii). Quadratic partial fractions $\dfrac{ax+b}{x^2+px+q}$ are retained if we wish to avoid complex numbers in the case when $p^2<4q$. Here there are two real undetermined coefficients in the numerator. Paradoxically the values of a and b are readily found by resorting to complex roots and proceeding as in (i). Multiply throughout by $x-\alpha-i\beta$ where $\alpha+i\beta$ is a complex root of $x^2+px+q=0$ and then put $x=\alpha+i\beta$.

Example. $$\frac{x^3}{(x+1)^3(x^2+4x+5)} = \frac{A}{(x+1)^3} + \frac{ax+b}{x^2+4x+5}.$$

Here A is a quadratic in x. The complex factors of x^2+4x+5 are $(x+2+i)(x+2-i)$. Multiply by $x+2+i$ and put $x=-2-i$. Then

$$\frac{(-2-i)^3}{(-1-i)^3(-2i)} = \frac{a(-2-i)+b}{-2i}.$$

This reduces, since $i^2=-1$, to $9/4-13i/4 = b-2a-ai$.

Since a and b are real, we have $b-2a=9/4$, $a=13/4$, and so $b=35/4$. Also $A = -\dfrac{13}{4}x^2 - \dfrac{9}{2}x - \dfrac{7}{4}$.

Case (iv). The real partial fraction $\dfrac{A}{(x^2+px+q)^r}$ may occur, where $p^2<4q$. Since the denominator is of degree $2r$, that of A may be $2r-1$ or less. On dividing A repeatedly by $X = x^2+px+q$, let the remainders be $R_1, R_2, \ldots$. Then the fraction can be written

$$\frac{R_r}{X^r} + \frac{R_{r-1}}{X^{r-1}} + \ldots + \frac{R_1}{X}.$$

Such remainders R are linear and real. Hence the original

rational function has been reduced to a sum of terms of the following possible types :

$$q(x),\ \frac{a}{x-a},\ \frac{a}{(x-a)^r},\ \frac{ax+b}{x^2+px+q},\ \frac{ax+b}{(x^2+px+q)^r}.$$

If the coefficients in the original function $f(x)/\phi(x)$ are complex, cases (iii) and (iv) are unimportant. They are significant when we wish to express a real function in its simplest partial fractions.

The following examples suggest further aspects of the subject.

1. $$\frac{2x}{x^2+4}=\frac{1}{x+2i}+\frac{1}{x-2i}:\quad \frac{8x}{4x^2-3}=\frac{2}{2x+\sqrt{3}}+\frac{2}{2x-\sqrt{3}}.$$

2. $$\frac{5-x}{(x-1)(x^2-3)}=\frac{ax+b}{x^2-3}+\frac{c}{x-1},$$ find the constants a, b, c.

This is the form to use if we wish to avoid irrational real numbers. Multiply by $x-1$ and put $x=1$; then $c=-2$. Multiply by $x-\sqrt{3}$ and then put $x=\sqrt{3}$. Hence

$$\frac{5-\sqrt{3}}{(\sqrt{3}-1)2\sqrt{3}}=\frac{a\sqrt{3}+b}{2\sqrt{3}},$$ so that $5-\sqrt{3}=(\sqrt{3}-1)(a\sqrt{3}+b)$, or $5+b-3a=\sqrt{3}(1+b-a)$. From $x+\sqrt{3}$ we get the same result but with $-\sqrt{3}$ for $+\sqrt{3}$. Hence each side of this equation vanishes separately and we have $a=2$, $b=1$.

3. If $f(x)$ is of lower degree than $\phi(x)=(x-\alpha)(x-\beta)(x-\gamma)$, where α, β, γ are distinct, prove that

$$\frac{f(x)}{\phi(x)}=\begin{vmatrix}\frac{f(\alpha)}{x-\alpha} & \frac{f(\beta)}{x-\beta} & \frac{f(\gamma)}{x-\gamma}\\ \alpha & \beta & \gamma\\ 1 & 1 & 1\end{vmatrix}\div\begin{vmatrix}\alpha^2 & \beta^2 & \gamma^2\\ \alpha & \beta & \gamma\\ 1 & 1 & 1\end{vmatrix}$$

4. If $\alpha=\beta\neq\gamma$, prove the result corresponding to the above, where the second column of each determinant is replaced by the derivative of the first column with respect to α; that is, these columns become $\left\{\frac{\partial}{\partial\alpha}\frac{f(\alpha)}{x-\alpha},\ 1,\ 0\right\}$ and $\{2\alpha, 1, 0\}$ respectively.

20. Determinantal Form of Partial Fractions. If $f(x)$ is a polynomial of degree less than that of $\phi(x)$, which is supposed to have no repeated factors, we can resolve $f(x)/\phi(x)$ into the form

$$\frac{f(x)}{\phi(x)} = \begin{vmatrix} 1 & 1 & \dots & 1 \\ \alpha & \beta & \dots & \lambda \\ \alpha^2 & \beta^2 & \dots & \lambda^2 \\ \cdot & \cdot & \cdot & \cdot \\ \alpha^{n-2} & \beta^{n-2} & \dots & \lambda^{n-2} \\ \frac{f(\alpha)}{x-\alpha} & \frac{f(\beta)}{x-\beta} & \dots & \frac{f(\lambda)}{x-\lambda} \end{vmatrix} \div \begin{vmatrix} 1 & 1 & \dots & 1 \\ \alpha & \beta & \dots & \lambda \\ \alpha^2 & \beta^2 & \dots & \lambda^2 \\ \cdot & \cdot & \cdot & \cdot \\ \alpha^{n-2} & \beta^{n-2} & \dots & \lambda^{n-2} \\ \alpha^{n-1} & \beta^{n-1} & \dots & \lambda^{n-1} \end{vmatrix} . \quad (1)$$

For the denominator determinant, Δ say, is the n-rowed *alternant* (Aitken, *Determinants and Matrices*, p. 41) which has the $\frac{1}{2}n(n-1)$ linear factors such as $\beta-\alpha$. In fact

$$\begin{aligned} \Delta = \Delta(\alpha\beta\ldots\kappa\lambda) = (\beta-\alpha)(\gamma-\alpha)\ldots(\lambda-\alpha) \\ \times(\gamma-\beta)\ldots(\lambda-\beta) \\ \cdots\cdots \\ \times(\lambda-\kappa). \end{aligned} \quad (2)$$

Also the numerator determinant may be expanded according to its final row as

$$\Sigma \frac{Af(\alpha)}{x-\alpha}, \quad . \quad . \quad . \quad . \quad (3)$$

the summation being of n terms corresponding to α, β, ..., λ, where A is an alternant of $n-1$ letters. Hence the right-hand side of (1) possesses the typical term

$$\frac{\Delta(\alpha\beta\ldots\kappa)f(\lambda)}{\Delta(\alpha\beta\ldots\kappa\lambda)(x-\lambda)} \quad \text{or} \quad \frac{f(\lambda)}{(\lambda-\alpha)(\lambda-\beta)\ldots(\lambda-\kappa)(x-\lambda)} \quad (4)$$

which is precisely the term given by the last partial fraction of $f(x)/\phi(x)$. Symmetry shows that all the partial fractions are obtained in this way.

21. The Confluent Case of Partial Fractions. Let

$$\phi(x) = (x-\alpha)^r(x-\beta)^s\ldots, \qquad . \quad . \quad (1)$$

where α, β, ... are all distinct. We call this the *confluent* case, where r of the roots α may be regarded as originally distinct but tending to equality, s further roots β tending to equality, and so on. If in the above determinants two roots are made equal the quotient is indeterminate, but if in the second column of each determinant α is replaced by $\alpha+h$ and h is allowed to *tend* to zero, the quotient of the determinants may be evaluated. When the first r roots are confluent and equal to α we take

$$u, \ \frac{\partial u}{\partial \alpha}, \ \frac{1}{2!}\frac{\partial^2 u}{\partial \alpha^2}, \ \ldots, \ \frac{1}{(r-1)!}\frac{\partial^{r-1}u}{\partial \alpha^{r-1}} \qquad . \quad (2)$$

to be the first r elements of any row, in numerator and denominator determinants, where u denotes the original entry in the first column on the row in question; that is, we differentiate each column successively and divide by a suitable factorial as in Taylor's expansion. The next s columns are formed in the same way afresh from a new root β; and so on. For example, if $f(x)$ is a cubic or lower polynomial,

$$\frac{f(x)}{(x-\alpha)^3(x-\beta)} = \begin{vmatrix} 1 & . & . & 1 \\ \alpha & 1 & . & \beta \\ \alpha^2 & 2\alpha & 1 & \beta^2 \\ \dfrac{f(\alpha)}{x-\alpha} & \left(\dfrac{f(\alpha)}{x-\alpha}\right)' & \dfrac{1}{2!}\left(\dfrac{f(\alpha)}{x-\alpha}\right)'' & \dfrac{f(\beta)}{x-\beta} \end{vmatrix} \div \begin{vmatrix} 1 & . & . & 1 \\ \alpha & 1 & . & \beta \\ \alpha^2 & 2\alpha & 1 & \beta^2 \\ \alpha^3 & 3\alpha^2 & 3\alpha & \beta^3 \end{vmatrix}, \qquad (3)$$

where accents denote differentiation with respect to α.

Proof. Proceed by induction on n, the degree of the denominator $\phi(x)$, and arrange the cases for the same value of n in the lexicographical order of the partitions $\{rs\ldots t\}$, where $r+s+\ldots+t = n$. The ordinary case is $\{11\ldots1\}$, and all other cases are confluent. For $n = 4$

the order is therefore {1111}, {211}, {22}, {31}, {4}. Any confluent case $\{...p\}$ or $\{...p1...\}$, where p is the last index exceeding unity, is derivable from an earlier case $\{...(p-1)1\}$ or $\{...(p-1)11...\}$ by letting the index $p-1$ merge with the next succeeding unit index.

Now assume the truth of the theorem for this earlier case, letting $(x-\gamma)^{p-1}(x-\delta)$ be the factors in $\phi(x)$ answering to the indices $p-1$, 1 which become confluent when $\delta = \gamma+h$ and $h \to 0$. The final entry of the column answering to $x-\delta$ in the upper determinant will then be

$$\frac{f(\delta)}{x-\delta} = \frac{f(\gamma+h)}{x-\gamma-h} =$$

$$\frac{f(\gamma)}{x-\gamma} + h\left(\frac{f(\gamma)}{x-\gamma}\right)' + \ldots + \frac{h^{p-1}}{(p-1)!}\left(\frac{f(\gamma)}{x-\gamma}\right)^{(p-1)} + \ldots.$$

Here every term before the pth in the series will disappear, by subtracting a suitable multiple of one of the $p-1$ columns just preceding—for similar series on each row of either determinant. So these may be discarded. After cancelling the factor h^{p-1} from both determinants and then letting $h \to 0$, the required result follows.

Example. Replace the third columns in (3) above by $\{1, \gamma, \gamma^2, f(\gamma)/(x-\gamma)\}$ and $\{1, \gamma, \gamma^2, \gamma^3\}$, and the left-hand expression by $f(x)/(x-a)^2(x-\beta)(x-\gamma)$. Assuming the truth of this identity, let $\gamma = a+h$. The third columns are now

$$\begin{matrix} 1 \\ a+h \\ (a+h)^2 \\ u+h\dfrac{\partial u}{\partial a}+\dfrac{h^2}{2!}\dfrac{\partial^2 u}{\partial a^2}+\ldots \end{matrix} \qquad \text{and} \qquad \begin{matrix} 1 \\ a+h \\ (a+h)^2 \\ (a+h)^3, \end{matrix}$$

where $u = f(a)/(x-a)$. The operation $\mathrm{col}_3-\mathrm{col}_1-h\mathrm{col}_2$, followed by cancelling h^2 and then putting $h = 0$, yields at once the result desired, corresponding to Case (ii) of **19**, p. **41**.

Corollary. We append a proof, by a similar induction, of the theorem on the value of the confluent alternant :

$$\Delta(a^r\beta^s\gamma^p \ldots \lambda^t) = \Pi(\beta-a)^{rs},$$

where the index rs is the product of the corresponding indices in Δ.

Proof. It is understood that $r+s+\ldots+t = n$, that $\alpha, \beta, \ldots, \lambda$ are distinct, and that the blocks of confluent columns are arranged as in the denominator determinant above. Let $p(>1)$ be the final confluent index.

Assuming the truth of the theorem for the partition $\{\ldots(p-1)1\ldots\}$ we have, say,

$$\Delta(\ldots\gamma^{p-1}\delta\ldots) = (\delta-\gamma)^{p-1}(\gamma-\alpha)^{r(p-1)}(\delta-\alpha)^{r}\psi,$$

where the product index $p-1$ is obtained from the indices of γ and δ in Δ, and ψ denotes all remaining factors. Let $\delta = \gamma+h$, so that the right-hand expression becomes

$$h^{p-1}(\gamma-\alpha)^{r(p-1)}(\gamma+h-\alpha)^{r}\psi.$$

Divide by h^{p-1} as before and let $h\to 0$. The left becomes the required new confluent determinant, and the right is a product of factors such as

$$(\gamma-\alpha)^{rp-r+r} = (\gamma-\alpha)^{rp}$$

which involve γ with α or any other root distinct from γ, together with factors such as $(\beta-\alpha)^{rs}$ which are unchanged throughout the process.

Examples. 1. In the denominator of (3) above, the value is

$$(\beta-\alpha)^3 = \Delta(\alpha\alpha\alpha\beta) = \Delta(\alpha^3\beta).$$

On the other hand, $\Delta(\alpha^2\beta\gamma) = (\gamma-\alpha)^2(\beta-\alpha)^2(\gamma-\beta)$.

2. $\Delta(\alpha^4\beta^3\gamma^2) = (\beta-\alpha)^{12}(\gamma-\alpha)^8(\gamma-\beta)^6$.

3. Integrate with respect to x: $f(x)/(x-\alpha)(x-\beta)(x-\gamma)$, $f(x)/(x-\alpha)^2(x-\beta)$, $f(x)/(x-\alpha)^3$. (Replace $f(\alpha)/(x-\alpha)$ throughout by $f(\alpha)\log(x-\alpha)$ in the determinantal formulæ equivalent to the sum of partial fractions.)

22. The Expansion of a Rational Function. Partial fractions give a means of expanding a function of x in ascending or descending powers of x. We shall illustrate this for the simple case when all the factors of $\phi(x)$ are distinct. Let

$$\frac{f(x)}{\phi(x)}=\frac{a}{x-\alpha}+\frac{b}{x-\beta}+\ldots+\frac{l}{x-\lambda}.$$

Now $a/(x-\alpha)=a(x^{-1}+\alpha x^{-2}+\alpha^2x^{-3}+\alpha^3x^{-4}+\ldots)$, . (1)

provided that this series converges, which happens if $|x|>|\alpha|$. This means that x is numerically greater than α if both are real, and that the modulus of x exceeds that of α if both are complex. For a proof we may refer to any text on analysis. We may regard the statement just written as a geometrical progression summed to infinity or equally well as an example of the binomial expansion of $ax^{-1}(1-\alpha x^{-1})^{-1}$.

Now take $|x|$ greater than the greatest among $|\alpha|$, $|\beta|$, ..., $|\lambda|$, expand each fraction, and add the results. Then

$$R(x)=f(x)/\phi(x)=(\Sigma a)x^{-1}+(\Sigma a\alpha)x^{-2}+(\Sigma a\alpha^2)x^{-3}+\ldots, \quad (2)$$

and this is the development of $R(x)$ in descending powers of x, valid for sufficiently large values of $|x|$.

Similarly, when $|x|<|\alpha|$ we have

$$a/(x-\alpha)=-a(\alpha^{-1}+\alpha^{-2}x+\alpha^{-3}x^2+\ldots). \quad (3)$$

Hence for sufficiently small values of x, in fact when $|x|$ is less than each of $|\alpha|$, $|\beta|$, ..., $|\lambda|$, we have the corresponding expansion in ascending powers of x:

$$R(x)=f(x)/\phi(x)=-\Sigma a\alpha^{-1}-(\Sigma a\alpha^{-2})x-(\Sigma a\alpha^{-3})x^2-\ldots. \quad (4)$$

Unless one or other of α, β, ..., λ vanishes this expansion is possible. Therefore if x is not a factor of $\phi(x)$ we may expand $f(x)/\phi(x)$ in ascending or descending series of powers of x, for suitably small or large values of x. The same applies when $\phi(x)$ has repeated roots, where the work may be carried out on terms such as $a(x-\alpha)^{-r}$ by the binomial theorem. If, however, x occurs as a factor in

$\phi(x)$, we remove the x before making an ascending expansion, and afterwards replace it.

Example. $$\frac{x-2}{x^3(x^2-1)} = \frac{1}{x^3}\{(2-x)(1-x^2)^{-1}\}$$
$$= x^{-3}(2-x+2x^2-x^3+\ldots)$$
$$= 2x^{-3}-x^{-2}+2x^{-1}-1+2x-\ldots.$$

Such a series, involving both ascending and descending powers of x, is called a *Laurent* expansion. Here there is necessarily a finite number of negative powers and an infinite number of positive powers.

For a descending expansion there is no restriction on the denominator. In this example it is

$$x^{-4}-2x^{-5}+x^{-6}-\ldots.$$

It is very useful to notice that the leading term in either expansion is given by the dominating terms of $f(x)$ and $\phi(x)$. In ascending series the dominating term is the lowest in powers of x: in descending it is the highest.

Examples. 1. $$\frac{x}{x^2-3x+2} = \frac{a}{x-1} + \frac{b}{x-2},$$

where $a = -1$, $b = 2$, and this on expansion gives

$$-(x^{-1}+x^{-2}+x^{-3}+\ldots)+2(x^{-1}+2x^{-2}+4x^{-3}+\ldots)$$
$$= x^{-1}+3x^{-2}+7x^{-3}+\ldots+(2^n-1)x^{-n}+\ldots,$$

if $x>2$ or <-2 when real; or if $|x|>2$ when x is complex.

Again

$$\frac{1}{1-x}-\frac{2}{2-x} = (1-x)^{-1}-(1-\tfrac{1}{2}x)^{-1}$$
$$= (1+x+x^2+\ldots)-(1+\tfrac{1}{2}x+\tfrac{1}{4}x^2+\ldots)$$
$$= \tfrac{1}{2}x+\tfrac{3}{4}x^2+\ldots+(1-2^{-n})x^n+\ldots,$$

if $-\tfrac{1}{2}<x<\tfrac{1}{2}$ when x is real; or if $|x|<\tfrac{1}{2}$ when x is complex.

2. Expand $x^4/(x^2-1)$ in ascending and also in descending powers of x. Is a Laurent expansion possible here ?

23. Recurring Series. When x is not a factor of $\phi(x)$, any rational function $R(x)$ may be expanded as above in powers of x. Suppose, therefore, that

$$f(x)/\phi(x) = p_0+p_1x+p_2x^2+\ldots+p_nx^n+\ldots.$$

The sequence of coefficients $p_0, p_1, p_2, \ldots$ is then called a *recurring* sequence or series. Such a series is characterized by a *scale of relation*, which means that, after a certain value n_0 of n, each coefficient p_n is formed in exactly the same way by a linear combination of its r immediate predecessors.

A scale of order $r = 1$ is given by $p_n = ap_{n-1}$, where a is constant and $n = 1, 2, 3, \ldots$ in succession. A scale of order 2 is given by $p_n = ap_{n-1}+bp_{n-2}$, where both a and b are constant: and so on. It is easy to prove that if $\phi(x)$ is of degree r the scale is of order r. The proof is left as an exercise for the reader, but is here illustrated when $r = 2$.

Let $$f(x)/\phi(x) = q(x)+r(x)/\phi(x)$$

in the usual way: then $q(x)$ is a polynomial which may interfere with the recurrence law for the first few terms, but $r(x)/\phi(x)$ gives the recurring series proper. We have, say, when x is suitably small,

$$\begin{aligned} r(x)/\phi(x) &= (cx+d)/(x^2+gx+h) \\ &= u_0+u_1x+u_2x^2+u_3x^3+\ldots, \end{aligned}$$

where we assume that $h\neq0$ since $\phi(0)\neq0$. Multiply throughout by x^2+gx+h and equate corresponding coefficients of x^0, x^1, x^2, ... on both sides of the resulting identity. Thus

$$\begin{aligned} d &= u_0\,h, & 0 &= u_2\,h+u_1\,g+u_0, \\ c &= u_1\,h+u_0\,g, & 0 &= u_3\,h+u_2\,g+u_1, \\ & & 0 &= u_n\,h+u_{n-1}\,g+u_{n-2},\ n>1. \end{aligned}$$

Since $h\neq0$ this gives a recurrence relation for u_n in terms of u_{n-1} and u_{n-2}, where $n = 2, 3, 4, \ldots$.

Conversely, we may sum a given recurring series to n

terms or to infinity (i) if the scale of relation is given, or (ii) if sufficient terms are given so as to reveal a scale unambiguously.

(i) Let $s = u_0+u_1x+u_2x^2+...+u_nx^n+...$, where u_0, u_1 are given, and also $u_n = au_{n-1}+bu_{n-2}$ for $n = 2, 3, ...$. Multiply throughout by ax and also by bx^2. Thus

$$\begin{aligned} axs &= au_0x+au_1x^2+...+au_{n-1}x^n+... \\ bx^2s &= \qquad\quad bu_0x^2+...+bu_{n-2}x^n+.... \end{aligned}$$

Hence by subtraction, carried out by powers of x,

$$(1-ax-bx^2)s = u_0+(u_1-au_0)x,$$

since every further coefficient of a power of x disappears owing to the scale of relation. Thus

$$s = \frac{u_0+(u_1-au_0)x}{1-ax-bx^2}$$

which is a rational proper fraction with a quadratic denominator ($r = 2$). To sum the series to n terms we proceed in the same way, but retain the non-vanishing terms involving x^{n+1} and x^{n+2}.

The procedure is palpably a generalization of the well-known method of summing a geometrical progression: indeed the latter is the case of a recurring series for which $r = 1$.

(ii) Given $r = 2$ and the series $1+3x+7x^2+15x^3+...$, to find the general term, the scale of relation, and the rational function s.

Assume $u_n = au_{n-1}+bu_{n-2}$; then $7 = 3a+b$, $15 = 7a+3b$. Hence $a = 3$, $b = -2$. Now proceed as before:

$$(1-3x+2x^2)s = 1+(3-3)x = 1.$$

Thus

$$\begin{aligned} s = \frac{1}{1-3x+2x^2} &= -\frac{1}{1-x}+\frac{2}{1-2x} \\ &= 1+3x+7x^2+...+(2^{n+1}-1)x^n+.... \end{aligned}$$

The general term is here shown.

Examples. The reader should take simple rational functions such as $(2-3x)/(1-5x+6x^2)$, should expand them to several terms in ascending powers of x (using either partial fractions or ordinary division), and should then try to recover the rational function from the recurring series by the methods outlined in the present section.

1. Determine the scale of relation and the coefficient of the nth term and the sum to infinity of the recurring series

$$4-8x+28x^2-80x^3+\dots .$$

For what values of x can it be summed to infinity?

2. Sum to infinity $2+5x+13x^2+35x^3+\dots$.

3. Discuss the series $1+3x+6x^2+10x^3+15x^4+21x^5+\dots$.

4. Show that

$$1+x\cos\theta+x^2\cos 2\theta+x^3\cos 3\theta+\dots$$

is a recurring series. So too is the corresponding series with each cosine replaced by a sine.

$$[u_n-2u_{n-1}\cos\theta+u_{n-2}=0].$$

5. If $|x|<1$ the sum to infinity of the above cosine series is

$$(1-x\cos\theta)\,/\,(1-2x\cos\theta+x^2).$$

6. Discuss the hyperbolic cosine and sine series corresponding to (4).

[Answers 1. $1-(-3)^n$, $4/(1+2x-3x^2)$, $|x|<\frac{1}{3}$.
2. $(2-5x)\,/\,(1-5x+6x^2)$. 3. $r=3$; $(1-x)^{-3}$.]

CHAPTER IV

THE FUNDAMENTAL THEOREM OF ALGEBRA

24. Statement of the Theorem. The basic theorem regarding algebraic equations may be stated as follows: Every equation

$$f(z) = z^n + a_1 z^{n-1} + a_2 z^{n-2} + \ldots + a_n = 0$$

in which the coefficients are arbitrary, real or complex numbers has at least one root $z = a + ib$, where a and b are real.

The first satisfactory proof of this theorem was given by Gauss (*Werke*, iii. 1) in his dissertation: *Demonstratio nova theorematis omnem functionem algebraicam unius variabilis in factores reales primi vel secundi gradus resolvi posse* (Helmsted, 1799). Gauss incidentally criticized the earlier defective proofs put forward by D'Alembert, Euler, and Lagrange. Gauss gave two further proofs in 1815 and 1816, but returned to his original method in 1849. A new proof was given by Cauchy (*Cours d'analyse algébrique*, ch. x, 1821), and later by Sturm (*Journ. de Mathématique*, i. 1836).

Although this theorem is fundamental for algebra, its proof belongs to the theory of analytic functions, which is a branch of analysis. The simplest proof runs as follows: $f(z)$ vanishes if $1/f(z)$ is infinite. Now $1/f(z)$ is an analytic function of z and, according to a theorem of Liouville, must either be a constant or else become infinite at one or more values of z. Hence $f(z)$ vanishes at least once. Liouville's theorem allows this value of z to be either infinite or finite. Now $f(z) \to \infty$ if $z \to \infty$; hence the value in question can only be finite. This proves the theorem.

A direct appeal to contour integration may be made which obviates the use of Liouville's theorem. The reader will find the matter discussed in textbooks on analysis; for example, MacRobert, *Functions of a Complex Variable* (1917), pp. 67-69, Phillips, *Functions of a Complex Variable* (1940), p. 113.

The original method of Gauss may be sketched as follows: Let $z = x+iy$

and $$f(z) = f(x+iy) = u(x, y)+iv(x, y),$$

where the polynomial $f(z)$ has been separated into two parts, real and imaginary. For instance,

$$z^3+2z+3 = (x+iy)^3+2(x+iy)+3.$$

Here $$u = x^3-3xy^2+2x+3, \quad v = 3x^2y-y^3+2y.$$

Both functions u and v are polynomials in x and y whose coefficients are real. Now suppose the curves $u = 0$, $v = 0$ to be drawn, for Cartesian coordinates x and y. If we can show that these curves intersect at a real finite point $P = (x, y)$, then at this point both the polynomials u and v vanish simultaneously. Hence $f(z)$ vanishes, and the point P represents a root $z = x+iy$ of the original equation $f(z) = 0$.

Now let $x = r \cos \theta$, $y = r \sin \theta$. Then

$$z = r(\cos \theta+i \sin \theta),$$

and by Demoivre's theorem $z^n = r^n(\cos n\theta+i \sin n\theta)$. Hence

$$u = r^n\cos n\theta+r^{n-1}(\ldots)+\ldots, \; v = r^n\sin n\theta+r^{n-1}(\ldots)+\ldots .$$

The polar coordinate forms of the curves may therefore be written

$$\cos n\theta+r^{-1}X = 0, \; \sin n\theta+r^{-1}Y = 0,$$

where X and Y are terms in cosines and sines of multiples of θ, with powers of r in the denominators. If r is large we obtain $\cos n\theta = 0$, $\sin n\theta = 0$ as approximations to the curves, that is to say, radii from the origin at equal angles $2\pi/n$ starting from $\theta = \frac{1}{2}\pi$ for the cosine, and $\theta = 0$ for the sine. If with centre at the origin O a circle $r = R$ is drawn with a large radius R, and a regular polygon $ABC...$ is inscribed, with $4n$ vertices beginning at $\theta = 0$, the above results mean that, as $R \to \infty$, the curves $u = 0$, $v = 0$ must approximate to the alternate radii OB, OD, ...

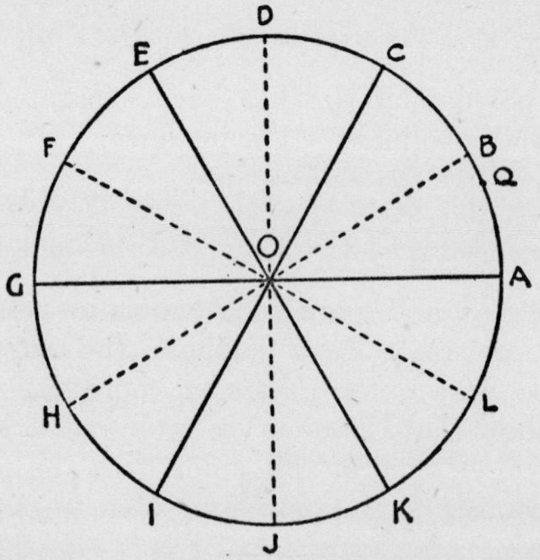

for u, and OA, OC, ... for v. An asymptote of the u curve would be parallel to OB and at a finite distance from OB. Thus it would cross the circumference ABC at a point Q such that the arc QB would remain finite while QA would tend to infinity, as $OB = R \to \infty$. Similarly for each vertex. Hence when R is large enough the u curve runs out of the circle near the n points B, D, ..., while the v curve runs out near the alternate points A, C, ...

Within the circle the curves are continuous, so that the $2n$ points near B, D, ... on the u curve must link up in pairs by means of n arcs, however complicated or twisted. Similarly for the v curve. It is topologically impossible to draw such arcs, starting at alternate circumferential points for u and v, without at least one crossing of a u arc with a v arc. Such a crossing gives the required point P and proves the theorem.

The above is a sketch of the proof. It obviously involves a knowledge of the algebraic curve, given by a real polynomial in x and y, and particularly the property that each arc of such a curve is continuous. The proof depends ultimately on the property that if Q, R, S, T are four points in order on a circle, a continuous path from Q to S within the circle must cross a continuous path from R to T.

25. The Product Form of an Algebraic Equation. Let us now return to the notation $f(x)$ for a polynomial, where x may be real or complex. The fundamental theorem has shown that a root α of the nth degree equation

$$f(x) = a_0x^n + a_1x^{n-1} + a_2x^{n-2} + \ldots + a_{n-1}x + a_n = 0$$

always exists; that is, $f(\alpha) = 0$. Now perform the division $f(x) \div (x-\alpha)$. We may write as before

$$f(x) = q(x)(x-\alpha) + r(x).$$

Since the divisor is linear the remainder is either a constant or zero. Thus $r(x) = c$, where c is a constant which may be zero. Now put $x = \alpha$ in the identity, which becomes $f(\alpha) = c$. Hence c vanishes with $f(\alpha)$, so that $x-\alpha$ is a factor of $f(x)$, whenever α is a root of $f(x) = 0$. From the first step of the actual division we notice that $q(x)$ is a polynomial with a_0x^{n-1} for leading term. Hence $f(x)$ takes the form

$$f(x) = (x-\alpha)(a_0x^{n-1} + b_1x^{n-2} + \ldots + b_{n-1}).$$

(Actually $b_1 = a_0\alpha + a_1$, $b_2 = a_0\alpha^2 + a_1\alpha + a_2$, etc.) By the fundamental theorem, $q(x) = 0$ also must have a root β, such that $x-\beta$ is a factor of $q(x)$. Hence

$$f(x) = (x-\alpha)(x-\beta)(a_0x^{n-2} + c_1x^{n-3} + \ldots + c_{n-2}).$$

The process may be repeated on the quotient until the final quotient is a constant, a_0 in fact. This happens when n such linear factors have been segregated. Thus we shall have

$$f(x) = a_0(x-\alpha)(x-\beta)\ldots(x-\lambda), \quad a_0 \neq 0,$$

where the n numbers $\alpha, \beta, \ldots, \lambda$ are called the n roots of the equation $f(x) = 0$. We have reduced $f(x)$ to its product form, or have resolved the polynomial into n linear factors.

Example. $\qquad f(x) = 2x^3-5x^2-9x+18.$

Here $f(3) = 0$, so that $x-3$ is a factor. We have, by division or by Horner's method,

$$\begin{aligned} f(x) &= (2x^2+x-6)(x-3) \\ &= (2x-3)(x+2)(x-3) \\ &= 2\left(x-\frac{3}{2}\right)(x+2)(x-3) \end{aligned}$$

where the roots are $\frac{3}{2}$, -2, 3. We note that the leading coefficient, $a_0 = 2$, survives as a factor in the final resolution.

26. Repeated Factors. Equal Roots. It may happen that some of the numbers $\alpha, \beta, \ldots, \lambda$ are equal. If exactly r of them are equal to α then we say that α is a root repeated r times, or is an r-fold root. Clearly $(x-\alpha)^r$ is then a factor of $f(x)$. Allowing for such repetitions we have now expressed $f(x)$ as

$$f(x) = a_0(x-\alpha)^r(x-\beta)^s\ldots(x-\lambda)^t,$$

where $r+s+\ldots+t = n$. Hence the indices $r, s, \ldots, t$ form a partition of n, and the simple or unrepeated case corresponds to the partition $\{11\ldots1\}$. Obviously $f(x)$ may have either one, two, ... or n distinct linear factors: it cannot have more, for this would imply a leading term a_0x^m in $f(x)$ of degree exceeding n.

Again, if θ is any number distinct from $\alpha, \beta, \ldots, \lambda$ then each of $\theta-\alpha, \theta-\beta, \ldots$ is non-zero. Hence

$$f(\theta) = a_0(\theta-\alpha)^r(\theta-\beta)^s\ldots(\theta-\lambda)^t \neq 0,$$

so that $f(\theta) \neq 0$ and θ is not a root of the equation. We have found n roots (allowing for repetitions among them): we see that no other number is a root. Hence there are exactly n roots of the equation.

This completes the result of **13**, where it was proved by rational methods that the equation $f(x) = 0$ could not have more than n roots (p. 23). Apart from the order in which the factors occur the resolution of $f(x)$ into its factors is unique.

The following theorem concerning an equation with repeated roots is important: *When the* $\mathrm{n^{th}}$ *degree equation* $\mathrm{f(x)} = 0$ *has exactly* r *roots equal to* α *then* f(x) *and its first, second, ...,* $\mathrm{(r-1)^{th}}$ *derivatives vanish at* $\mathbf{x} = \alpha$, *but its* $\mathrm{r^{th}}$ *and following, up to the* $\mathrm{n^{th}}$ *inclusive, do not.*

Proof. In this case we can write $f(x) = (x-\alpha)^r\psi(x)$ where $\psi(\alpha) \neq 0$. Hence, by differentiation,

$$f'(x) = r(x-\alpha)^{r-1}\psi(x) + (x-\alpha)^r\psi'(x),$$

so that $f'(x)$ contains the factor $(x-\alpha)^{r-1}$. Its cofactor is $r\psi(x)+(x-\alpha)\psi'(x)$, and, when $x = \alpha$, this is equal to $r\psi(\alpha)$ which is non-zero by hypothesis. Thus the first derivative contains the factor $x-\alpha$ exactly $r-1$ times. The same method shows that $f''(x)$ contains the factor $r-2$ times: and so on until the $(r-1)^{th}$ derivative contains the factor once, and the rth is free from the factor. Thus the theorem is proved.

Example. $f(x) = x^3-4x^2+5x-2,$

$f'(x) = 3x^2-8x+5, \quad f''(x) = 6x-8.$

Here $f(x) = (x-1)^2(x-2), f'(x) = (x-1)(3x-5)$, and $f(1) = 0$, $f'(1) = 0, f''(1) \neq 0$. The root 1 is repeated twice.

We may note that if, as here, $f'(x)$ can readily be factorized, it is easy to find the repeated roots. The second zero 5/3 of $f'(x)$ is of course not a root of $f(x)$: nor is the single zero of $f''(x)$.

The geometrical interpretation of a repeated root is simple. If $f'(a) = 0$ the gradient of the graph is zero at $x = a$, and if also $f(a) = 0$ the graph meets the axis of x at the point $(a, 0)$. Hence if a is a repeated root of the equation $f(x) = 0$ the graph touches the axis of x at $(a, 0)$. It is worth while drawing the graphs of f, f', and f'' in order to gain insight into the behaviour of f at a repeated zero. Furthermore, by Taylor's theorem, we have

$$f(x) = f(a+x-a) = f(a)+(x-a)f'(a)+\ldots+ \frac{(x-a)^n}{n!} f^{(n)}(a).$$

If $f(a)$ and its first $r-1$ derivatives all vanish but not the rth, then $(x-a)^r$ is a factor of every term in this series and therefore of $f(x)$. Hence the converse of the above theorem is true.

An important corollary of the theorem, having reference to the G.C.M. of $f(x)$ and $f'(x)$, is as follows : *If* f(x) *contains the factor* x$-a$ *exactly* r *times, then* G(x), *the G.C.M. of* f(x) *and* f'(x), *contains the same factor exactly* r-1 *times, and* G(x) *is composed entirely of such repeated factors of* f(x).

Proof. If $f(a)$ and $f'(a)$ both vanish then $x-a$ is a common factor of $f(x)$ and $f'(x)$. Since it occurs to degree r in $f(x)$, it occurs to degree $r-1$ in $f'(x)$, so that $G(x)$ contains this factor to the power $r-1$ also.

Now $G(x)$ cannot contain a factor $x-\theta$ unless both $f(\theta)$ and $f'(\theta)$ vanish. Hence $G(x)$ can only be

$$(x-\alpha)^{r-1}(x-\beta)^{s-1}\ldots(x-\lambda)^{t-1}$$

where α, β, ..., λ all differ.

Again, if $f(x)$ is any given polynomial, not necessarily factorized, we can find both $f'(x)$ and $G(x)$ by the ordinary rational methods. Also we can write

$$f(x) = G(x)\, h(x)$$

where $h(x)$, the cofactor of $G(x)$ in $f(x)$, can be ascertained by long division. Every zero of $h(x)$ is manifestly a zero of $f(x)$, but it is more interesting to note that, conversely, every zero of $f(x)$ is also a zero of $h(x)$ and that $h(x)$ has no repeated factor. Indeed

$$h(x) = \frac{f(x)}{G(x)} = a_0 \frac{(x-\alpha)^r(x-\beta)^s\ldots(x-\lambda)^t}{(x-\alpha)^{r-1}(x-\beta)^{s-1}\ldots(x-\lambda)^{t-1}}$$
$$= a_0(x-\alpha)(x-\beta)\ldots(x-\lambda).$$

The equation $h(x) = 0$ is called the *reduced unrepeated form* of $f(x) = 0$. We note that if any index t is unity $G(x)$ has no corresponding factor.

In practice all repeated factors may be removed by this method, even if the separate factors $x-\alpha$ cannot easily be identified. If they can, so much the better.

Examples. 1. Solve

$$x^7-x^6-11x^5+11x^4+19x^3-19x^2-9x+9 = 0.$$

(The roots are 1, 1, 1, -1, -1, 3, -3.)

2. The reduced unrepeated form of

$$x^7-x^6+2x^5+2x^4-3x^3+3x^2-4$$

is $(x^3+x+2)(x-1)$. There are three pairs of repeated roots and one unrepeated.

27. Complex Roots of an Equation. Starting with the known fact that a quadratic with real coefficients may fail to have real roots, we can easily construct an equation of the nth degree with less than n real roots: thus $(x^2+1)(x^2+x+1) = 0$ is a quartic equation with no real roots; and $(x-1)(x^2+1)^2 = 0$ is a quintic with only one real root. We must therefore be prepared to consider complex roots of a real equation

$$f(x) = a_0x^n+a_1x^{n-1}+\ldots+a_n = 0,$$

where each coefficient a_i is real. Incidentally, we may merge the case of complex equations, where the a_i are complex, in that of the present case where the coefficients are real, by the method of **5**, Ex. 2, p. **11**. The roots of a complex equation of degree m may be regarded as roots of a real equation of, at most, degree $2m$.

Example. $x^2-ix-1-i=0$ is a complex quadratic whose roots are included among the three roots of the real cubic $x^3-x^2+2=0$.

Let us then confine ourselves to real equations. If $a+i\beta$ is any complex number we have

$$f(a+i\beta)=A+iB$$

where a, β, A and B are real. This result is obtained by a straightforward reduction due to replacing i^2 by -1 whenever it occurs. Since $(-i)^2=-1$ we should obtain in exactly the same way

$$f(a-i\beta)=A-iB$$

where A and B are the same as before.

Example.

$$a(a+i\beta)^2+b(a+i\beta)+c=a(a^2-\beta^2)+ba+c+i(2aa\beta+b\beta),$$
$$a(a-i\beta)^2+b(a-i\beta)+c=a(a^2-\beta^2)+ba+c-i(2aa\beta+b\beta).$$

Now suppose that $a+i\beta$ is a root of $f(x)=0$, so that $A+iB=0$. Since A and B are real, this is only possible when $A=0$, $B=0$. Hence $A-iB=0$, so that $f(a-i\beta)=0$, that is, $a-i\beta$ is also a root. Hence we have proved the following property :

All complex roots of a real equation occur in pairs, such as $a\pm i\beta$, which are conjugate complex numbers : the number of complex roots of a real equation is therefore even.

Since $(x-a-i\beta)(x-a+i\beta)=(x-a)^2+\beta^2$, which is real and positive whenever x is real, it follows that every real polynomial may be expressed in the form

$$f(x)=a_0(x-a)\dots(x^2+px+q)\dots$$
$$=a_0\Pi(x-a)\Pi(x^2+px+q),$$

where Π indicates a product of typical factors, and in each quadratic factor $p^2<4q$. This is a resolution into real factors, linear for each root a of $f(x) = 0$, and quadratic for each pair of conjugate complex roots. Of course there may be repetitions among the roots, but if a complex root is repeated, so is its conjugate, and so therefore is the real quadratic factor x^2+px+q.

In terms of real numbers we can now say that every real polynomial can be factorized into real linear or irresoluble quadratic factors, and that such a factorization is unique.

Examples. 1. Find the real factors of x^4+10x^2+169, x^6+1, $x^4-16x^2+40x-25$.

2. Solve the equation $27x^4-45x^2+26x-4 = 0$, given that it has a repeated root.

3. Find the reduced unrepeated form of the following equations :

(i) $x^4-18x^3+69x^2+108x+36 = 0$.

(ii) $x^4-10x^3+37x^2-60x+36 = 0$.

(Each equation has two pairs of repeated roots.)

4. Solve the equation $x^4-8x^3+16x^2-64x+64 = 0$, which has two roots of the type $\pm i\beta$.

5. The equation $x^4-4x^3+7x^2+6 = 0$ has no real roots.

(Consider $(x-1)^4 + (x+2)^2+1$.)

6. Find four real roots of $x^8-47x^4+1 = 0$.

7. Solve $(x-1)^7 = x^7-1$, which has two repeated roots.

[Answers :

2. Put $3x=y$; $x=\frac{1}{3}, \frac{1}{3}, -\frac{1}{3}(1\pm\sqrt{13})$.

4. $\pm 2\sqrt{2}i$, $4\pm 2\sqrt{2}$.

6. $\pm\frac{1}{2}(3\pm\sqrt{5})$.]

CHAPTER V

PROPERTIES OF THE COEFFICIENTS OF AN ALGEBRAIC EQUATION

28. The Elementary Symmetric Functions. Let α, β, ..., λ be the n roots of the equation

$$f(x) = a_0x^n+a_1x^{n-1}+\ldots+a_{n-1}x+a_n = 0,\ a_0\neq 0. \qquad (1)$$

Then $$f(x) = a_0(x-\alpha)(x-\beta)\ldots(x-\lambda). \qquad (2)$$

Equating these two expressions we have an identity which is true for all values of x; hence we may multiply out the bracket factors and equate coefficients of corresponding powers of x. Thus

$$\begin{aligned} a_0 & & &= \quad a_0, \\ a_0\Sigma\alpha &= a_0(\alpha+\beta+\ldots) & &= -\ a_1, \\ a_0\Sigma\alpha\beta &= a_0(\alpha\beta+\alpha\gamma+\ldots) & &= \quad a_2, \\ a_0\Sigma\alpha\beta\gamma &= a_0(\alpha\beta\gamma+\ldots) & &= -\ a_3, \\ & \ldots\ldots\ldots\ldots & & \\ a_0\alpha\beta\ldots\lambda & & &= (-)^n a_n, \end{aligned} \qquad (3)$$

or $\Sigma\alpha = -a_1/a_0$, $\Sigma\alpha\beta = a_2/a_0$, $\Sigma\alpha\beta\gamma = -a_3/a_0$, etc. These relations express the coefficients a_i in terms of the leading coefficient a_0 and of the *elementary symmetric functions* of the roots (Girard, 1629; Harriot, 1631; Vieta, 1646). The mth elementary symmetric function is the sum Σ of the combinations of the n letters α, β, ..., λ taken m at a time, so that Σ has $n_{(m)}$ terms, where

$$n_{(m)} = \binom{n}{m} = \frac{n!}{m!(n-m)!} = \frac{n(n-1)\ldots(n-m+1)}{1\,.\,2\,.\ldots m},$$

the well-known binomial coefficient. We may refer to these sums as the sums of m-ary products of the roots.

Examples.

For $ax^2+2bx+c$, $\Sigma\alpha = \alpha+\beta = -2b/a$, $\alpha\beta = c/a$.

For $a_0x^3+a_1x^2+a_2x+a_3$, $\Sigma\alpha = \alpha+\beta+\gamma = -a_1/a_0$,
$\Sigma\alpha\beta = \alpha\beta+\alpha\gamma+\beta\gamma = a_2/a_0$, $\alpha\beta\gamma = -a_3/a_0$.

For a quartic (biquadratic) $\Sigma\alpha\beta$ has six terms and $\Sigma\alpha\beta\gamma$ has four. It is important to become thoroughly familiar with these relations (3) for the cubic and quartic cases. Note that a_0 occurs in each denominator of a sum of m-ary products, and that the suffix in the numerator determines both the sign and the number of factors in each term of the series. This number is called the *weight* of the term and of the series and of the coefficient.

In particular cases care is needed, since the notation Σ is devised to help only in the general case when all the roots are distinct. For instance, if $f(x) = (x-a)^2(x-b)$, then $\Sigma\alpha = a+a-b = 2a-b$, $\Sigma\alpha\beta = a^2-2ab$, $\alpha\beta\gamma = -a^2b$.

The relations are of immediate help in the solution of an equation whenever the roots are rational, or integral, or satisfy simple relations, as when they are in arithmetical progression.

Examples. 1. If all the roots and coefficients are integers a_0 must be a factor of each a_i and each root is a factor of a_n.

Solve $x^3-6x^2+11x-6 = 0$ by trial.

2. Solve $x^3-5x^2-58x = 88$.

3. Solve $x^3-3ax^2+(3a^2-b^2)x-a(a^2-b^2) = 0$, having given that the roots are in arithmetical progression.

4. Solve $8x^3-52x^2+78x-27 = 0$, given that the roots are in geometrical progression.

5. Solve $x^4+x^3+7x^2+4x+12 = 0$, given that one of the roots is a pure imaginary.

(Take $a, b, \pm ic$ as roots. The roots are $\pm 2i$, $-\frac{1}{2}(1\pm i\sqrt{11}.)$

29. Allied Equations and Polynomials. It is an immediate consequence of the m-ary relations of **28** (3) that

$$a_0x^n+a_1x^{n-1}y+a_2x^{n-2}y^2+\ldots+a_{n-1}xy^{n-1}+a_ny^n$$
$$= a_0(x-\alpha y)(x-\beta y)\ldots(x-\lambda y). \quad . \quad . \quad . \quad . \quad (1)$$

This is called the *homogeneous* form of the identity due to factorizing the polynomial $f(x)$. Other variants of the same theme are obtained by putting $y = -1$, thus,

$$a_0x^n-a_1x^{n-1}+a_2x^{n-2}-\ldots+(-)^na_n$$
$$= a_0(x+\alpha)(x+\beta)\ldots(x+\lambda), \quad . \quad . \quad . \quad (2)$$

or again by writing 1 for x and x for y:

$$a_0+a_1x+a_2x^2+\ldots+a_nx^n$$
$$= a_0(1-\alpha x)(1-\beta x)\ldots(1-\lambda x). \quad . \quad . \quad (3)$$

The zeros of this reversed polynomial are α^{-1}, β^{-1}, ..., λ^{-1}, that is, the reciprocals of the roots of $f(x) = 0$.

Zero and Infinite Roots of an Equation. The equation $f(x) = 0$ has a zero root if, and only if, $a_n = 0$, as is obvious. When the last r coefficients vanish but the coefficient a_{n-r} does not, then there are manifestly r repeated zero roots. In this case the reversed equation just written down appears to have r infinite roots, since the root α of the original equation corresponds to α^{-1} in the reversed equation. Similarly, when the first r coefficients of $f(x)$ vanish but a_r does not, we might consider $f(x) = 0$ to have r infinite roots. This is, however, a sophisticated way of viewing the situation, since the equation is no longer of the nth degree but of the $(n-r)^{th}$ degree.

It is, however, more fruitful to consider a limiting case, and first to ask what is the effect on the roots if the coefficients vary slightly ? To answer this, let us consider the graph of $f(x)$ when each coefficient is numerically less than ϵ, supposed small. As on p. 18, we can take ϵ small enough to ensure that $f(x)$ will be less than any assigned small quantity. Let the ordinate of such a curve be called η, so that η is small. Now take any finite values of the a_i and alter them by adding these small coefficients. The resulting graph will differ vertically at (x, y) to an extent η, which may be positive or negative. Hence it must cross the axis of x at points which are near to the crossings of $f(x)$ on the axis: that is, the real roots of $f(x) = 0$ are altered slightly when the coefficients are so altered. Each real root is in fact a continuous function of the coefficients: so too is a complex root, but we shall not attempt to prove this.

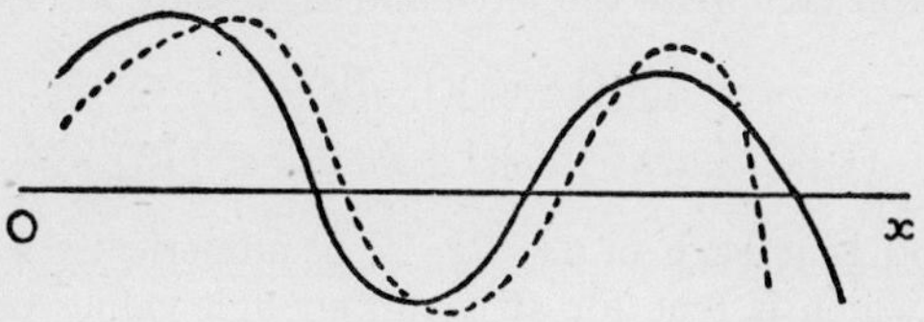

Suppose that $a_0 \neq 0$ but that $a_0 \to 0$, while $a_1 \to a \neq 0$, $a_n \to b \neq 0$ simultaneously. Let us consider the effect on the reversed equation

$$a_n x^n + a_{n-1} x^{n-1} + \ldots + a_1 x + a_0 = 0.$$

It will tend to a form for which one root is zero and the rest are non-zero. If one root α only of this equation tends to zero, then the sum of $(n-1)$-ary products of roots contains one term $\beta\gamma\ldots$ which remains finite, while the rest of the terms contain the factor α and consequently tend to zero. If two roots tend to zero, every term of the $(n-1)$-ary product sum tends to zero. Hence $a_1 \to 0$, which contradicts the supposition. Accordingly if $a_0 \to 0$ but a_1 does not tend to zero, then one root and one only of the reversed equation tends to zero, and one and one only of the original equation tends to infinity.

Example. Solve $\epsilon x^2 + 2x - 3 = 0$.

30. Further Symmetric Functions of the Roots. A second set of important symmetric functions of the roots of $f(x) = 0$ may be introduced as follows:

Definition.—The coefficient h_r of x^r in the expansion

$$a_0(a_0+a_1x+\ldots+a_nx^n)^{-1}$$
$$= h_0+h_1x+h_2x^2+\ldots+h_rx^r+\ldots \quad . \quad . \quad (1)$$

is called the homogeneous product symmetric function of order r in the roots of the equation

$$f(x) = a_0x^n+a_1x^{n-1}+\ldots+a_{n-1}x+a_n = 0.$$

We can in fact write the left-hand expression in (1) as

$$a_0\{a_0(1-\alpha x)(1-\beta x)\ldots\}^{-1}$$

or $$(1+\alpha x+\alpha^2x^2+\ldots)(1+\beta x+\beta^2x^2+\ldots)\ldots, \quad . \quad (2)$$

provided that each of αx, βx, ... is numerically less than unity, which is true for all small enough values of x. In which case by equating coefficients we have

$$h_0 = 1,\ h_1 = \Sigma\alpha,\ h_2 = \Sigma\alpha^2+\Sigma\alpha\beta,\ h_3 = \Sigma\alpha^3+\Sigma\alpha^2\beta+\Sigma\alpha\beta\gamma,$$

and so on. Obviously h_r is the sum of all distinct terms composed of exactly r factors α, β, ..., *allowing repetitions.* (These symmetric functions are sometimes referred to as sums of m-ary powers and products, sometimes as *aleph* functions of the roots, a name originally given by Wronski). The summations involve more terms, and are more complicated than those of the elementary symmetric functions, which we shall now denote by e_1, e_2, and so on. But the e and the h functions are equally important, and between them there runs a close parallelism. (See for example, Aitken, *Determinants and Matrices*, pp. 113-121, where the elementary symmetric functions are denoted by a_r.)

The number ${}_nH_r$ of terms in the summations h_r is given by putting $\alpha = \beta = \ldots = \lambda = 1$, since each term then reduces to unity. But this gives, instead of the identity (1),

$$(1-x)^{-n} = {}_nH_0+{}_nH_1x+{}_nH_2x^2+\ldots+{}_nH_rx^r+\ldots \quad . \qquad (3)$$

By the binomial theorem we find that

$${}_nH_r = (n+r-1)_{(r)} = \frac{n(n+1)(n+2)\ldots(n+r-1)}{1\,.\,2\,.\,3\,.\,\ldots\,.\,r}, \quad . \qquad (4)$$

which therefore gives the number of ways of choosing r things from n things when repetitions are allowed.

31. Relations between the e and the h Functions. From **29** (3) we have at once

$$\begin{aligned} F(x) &= (1-\alpha x)(1-\beta x)\ldots(1-\lambda x) \\ &= 1-e_1x+e_2x^2-\ldots+(-)^ne_nx^n, \end{aligned}$$

while

$$\{F(x)\}^{-1} = \{\Pi(1-\alpha x)\}^{-1} = 1+h_1x+h_2x^2+\ldots+h_rx^r+\ldots .$$

For convenience we may take $e_0 = 1$, $h_0 = 1$. Here we notice that the e-series is finite while the h-series is infinite. On multiplying them together we have the identity

$$1 = F(x)\{F(x)\}^{-1} = (1-e_1x+\ldots)(1+h_1x+\ldots),$$

so that the coefficient of each positive power in the expansion must vanish. Accordingly we have

$$\begin{aligned} &e_1-h_1 = 0, \\ &e_2-e_1h_1+h_2 = 0, \quad . \quad . \quad . \quad . \qquad (1) \\ &e_3-e_2h_1+e_1h_2-h_3 = 0, \end{aligned}$$

relations which are called Wronski's relations (Aitken, *Determinants and Matrices*, p. 114). Solving from these each way in turn, we have

$$\begin{aligned} e_1 &= h_1, & h_1 &= e_1, \\ e_2 &= h_1^2-h_2, & h_2 &= e_1^2-e_2, \quad . \quad . \qquad (2) \\ e_3 &= h_1^3-2h_1h_2+h_3, & h_3 &= e_1^3-2e_1e_2+e_3, \end{aligned}$$

and so on. Hence either set may be expressed rationally and integrally in terms of the other; and the interchangeable rôles of the e's and the h's in such formulae cannot fail to be noticed.

Example. Prove that

$$a_0 e_r = (-)^r a_r, \quad a_0 h_r + a_1 h_{r-1} + \ldots + a_r h_0 = 0.$$

32. The Sums of Powers Symmetric Functions. A third set of symmetric functions of the roots is the sums of powers:

$$\begin{aligned} s_1 &= \Sigma\alpha \ = \alpha+\beta+\ldots+\lambda, \\ s_2 &= \Sigma\alpha^2 = \alpha^2+\beta^2+\ldots+\lambda^2, \\ &\ldots\ldots\ldots\ldots\ldots\ldots \\ s_m &= \Sigma\alpha^m = \alpha^m+\beta^m+\ldots+\lambda^m. \end{aligned} \qquad (1)$$

It is possible to express each of these sums rationally and integrally in terms of the elementary symmetric functions e_r. The results are embodied in Newton's formulae (1707), which run as follows:

$$\begin{aligned} &a_0 s_1 + a_1 = 0, \\ &a_0 s_2 + a_1 s_1 + 2a_2 = 0, \\ &\ldots\ldots\ldots\ldots \\ &\ldots\ldots\ldots\ldots \\ &a_0 s_p + a_1 s_{p-1} + \ldots + a_{p-1} s_1 + p a_p = 0, \end{aligned} \qquad (2)$$

where of course $a_p = 0$ when p exceeds n. To establish these relations we calculate $f'(x)$ in terms both of the coefficients and of the roots, and then equate corresponding terms in powers of x. Now

$$f'(x) = n a_0 x^{n-1} + (n-1) a_1 x^{n-2} + \ldots + a_{n-1}.$$

Also
$$f'(x) = \frac{f(x)}{x-\alpha} + \frac{f(x)}{x-\beta} + \ldots + \frac{f(x)}{x-\lambda}, \qquad (3)$$

as is at once seen by differentiating the product form of

$f(x)$ in **25** (p. 60). Again, by ordinary long division we have

$$\frac{f(x)}{x-\alpha} = (a_0x^n + a_1x^{n-1} + \ldots + a_n)/(x-\alpha)$$

$$= a_0x^{n-1} + (a_0\alpha_1 + a_1)x^{n-2} + (a_0\alpha^2 + a_1\alpha + a_2)x^{n-3} + \ldots + (a_0\alpha^{n-1} + \ldots) \quad (4)$$

without remainder. The process yields an apparent remainder $f(\alpha)$ which of course vanishes. (The quotient just written down is indeed an alternative way of writing

$$a_0(x-\beta)(x-\gamma)\ldots(x-\lambda)$$

which would result from dividing the factorized form of $f(x)$ by $x-\alpha$.) Let a series similar to (4) be formed for each root in turn. This gives n such series, and their sum will therefore be equal to $f'(x)$, so that

$$f'(x) = na_0x^{n-1} + (a_0s_1 + na_1)x^{n-2} + (a_0s_2 + a_1s_1 + na_2)x^{n-3} + \ldots.$$

For example, when $n = 3$, the three terms involving x^{n-2} give $a_0\alpha + a_1 + a_0\beta + a_1 + a_0\gamma + a_1$ for coefficient, which is $a_0s_1 + 3a_1$. Similarly for the other terms.

On comparing coefficients in the original and in this final form of $f'(x)$ we have

$$(n-1)a_1 = a_0s_1 + na_1,\ (n-2)a_2 = a_0\,s_2 + a_1s_1 + na_2, \text{ etc.}$$

whence the first n of Newton's formulae at once follow.

Again, let $F(x) = a_0x^p + a_1x^{p-1} + \ldots + a_nx^{p-n}$, where p is a positive integer greater than n. Since x^{p-n} is a factor, and $f(x)$ is its cofactor, we infer that the roots of $F(x) = 0$ are α, β, ..., λ together with $p-n$ zeros. Hence the sums of powers of its roots are the same as for $f(x)$. By writing out the pth formula in Newton's relations for $F(x)$ according to the above method we obtain

$$a_0s_p + \ldots + a_ns_{p-n} + \ldots + pa_p = 0.$$

But all the coefficients subsequent to a_n are zero, so that

$$a_0s_p + a_1s_{p-1} + \ldots + a_ns_{p-n} = 0, \quad . \quad . \quad (5)$$

which is the form of Newton's relations for $p > n$.

The following alternative form of Newton's relations is easily deduced, since $a_0 e_r = (-)^r a_r$:

$$\begin{array}{ll} s_1 - e_1 = 0, & \text{whence } s_1 = e_1, \\ s_2 - e_1 s_1 + 2e_2 = 0, & s_2 = e_1^2 - 2e_2, \\ s_3 - e_1 s_2 + e_2 s_1 - 3e_3 = 0, & s_3 = e_1^3 - 3e_1 e_2 + 3e_3, \\ \cdots\cdots & \cdots\cdots\cdots \end{array} \qquad (6)$$

This shows that each of the s-functions may be expressed rationally and integrally in terms of the m-ary product sums of elementary symmetric functions of the roots. These equations were first given by J. Gregory in 1675 for the case of the septimic equation ($n = 7$) as far as s_7.

The first set of relations in (6) between the s and the e functions is linear in both sets of variables, and may accordingly be solved for either set in terms of the other. When this is done determinantally we find that

$$s_1 = e_1, \qquad e_1 = s_1,$$

$$s_2 = \begin{vmatrix} e_1 & 1 \\ 2e_2 & e_1 \end{vmatrix}, \qquad e_2 = \frac{1}{2!}\begin{vmatrix} s_1 & 1 \\ s_2 & s_1 \end{vmatrix},$$

$$s_3 = \begin{vmatrix} e_1 & 1 & . \\ 2e_2 & e_1 & 1 \\ 3e_3 & e_2 & e_1 \end{vmatrix}, \qquad e_3 = \frac{1}{3!}\begin{vmatrix} s_1 & 1 & . \\ s_2 & s_1 & 2 \\ s_3 & s_2 & s_1 \end{vmatrix}, \qquad . \qquad (7)$$

$$s_4 = \begin{vmatrix} e_1 & 1 & . & . \\ 2e_2 & e_1 & 1 & . \\ 3e_3 & e_2 & e_1 & 1 \\ 4e_4 & e_3 & e_2 & e_1 \end{vmatrix}, \qquad e_4 = \frac{1}{4!}\begin{vmatrix} s_1 & 1 & . & . \\ s_2 & s_1 & 2 & . \\ s_3 & s_2 & s_1 & 3 \\ s_4 & s_3 & s_2 & s_1 \end{vmatrix},$$

and so on.

If we apply the above reasoning to the equation

$$x^n + a_1 x^{n-1} + a_2 x^{n-2} + \ldots + a_n = 0 \quad . \quad . \quad (8)$$

where $a_0 = 1$, we have at once $\Sigma \alpha^2 = s_2 = a_1^2 - 2a_2$. If all the roots are real each α^2 is positive, so that $a_1^2 > 2a_2$. Therefore if $a_1^2 < 2a_2$ or $= 2a_2$ there must be some complex roots. This proves the following result:

The equation (8) *has at least one pair of conjugate complex roots whenever*

(1) $a_1^2 < 2a_2$, (2) $a_1^2 = 2a_2$, (3) $a_1 = 0$, $a_2 > 0$,
(4) $a_1 = a_2 = 0$.

It by no means follows that when $a_1^2 > 2a_2$ all the roots are real, as the case $x^2+6x+11 = 0$ shows. Here $36 > 22$ but the roots are complex.

33. Symmetric Functions in General. Any function of n arguments $\alpha, \beta, ..., \lambda$ which is unchanged by any interchange among the arguments is called symmetric. For example, x^2y+xy^2, $\sin(x+y)$, $(x-y)^2$ are symmetric functions of x and y, but the function $x-y$ is not, since it differs from $y-x$. We have already considered several symmetric functions of the roots of an equation, and the fact that the coefficients of

$$x^n+a_1x^{n-1}+...+a_n = 0$$

are instances of such functions suggests their importance. Actually they play a fundamental part in many branches of higher mathematics, beginning with the theoretical solution of a cubic or higher equation.

Fundamental Theorem on Symmetric Functions. Every rational integral symmetric function of the n arguments $\alpha, \beta, ..., \lambda$ can be expressed as a rational integral function of the n elementary symmetric functions $e_1, e_2, ..., e_n$.

Proof. This follows by induction. Every such symmetric function S is a sum of terms $c\alpha^r\beta^s...\lambda^t$, where c is a constant. Select from S a term of lowest degree in the n arguments, that is, one for which the sum $r+s+...+t$ is least. Collect together all the terms which are symmetrical with it and necessarily have the same coefficient c_1, calling the sum of these c_1S_1. Since S is symmetrical and S_1 also, then manifestly $S-c_1S_1$ is so too. Repeat the process on this by collecting out of it a symmetrical set c_2S_2: and continue until the whole expression S is exhausted. This expresses S as a finite sum of monomial symmetric functions such as S_1. Thus

$$S = c_1S_1+c_2S_2+\ldots+c_kS_k, \text{ where } S_1 = \Sigma\alpha^r\beta^s\ldots\lambda^t.$$

For example, when

$$S = x^3-3xy+x^2y+y^3+2x+2y+xy^2,$$
$$S_1 = x+y,\quad S_2 = xy,\quad S_3 = x^2y+xy^2,\quad S_4 = x^3+y^3.$$

Among the terms such as S_i several may have the same degree p, as S_3, S_4 in the above example. When this happens we arrange these terms in ascending lexical order of the partition $\{rs\ldots t\}$ belonging to the positive integer p, lower indices taking precedence over higher (see p. 2) and $r\leqslant s\leqslant\ldots\leqslant t$. Corresponding to each partition there is one monomial symmetric function, and vice versa.

If we can prove the theorem for a monomial symmetric function of any degree p and any set of indices $\{rs\ldots t\}$ it must then be true for every S. We prove it for monomials by induction, assuming it true for all monomials of lower degree than p, and for those with an equal p but an earlier partition in the lexical order.

Write $\alpha^r\beta^s\ldots\lambda^t = (\alpha\beta\ldots\lambda)^r(\beta\gamma\ldots\lambda)^{s-r}\ldots = T$, which can be done since we have assumed, without loss of generality, that $r\leqslant s\leqslant\ldots\leqslant t$.

For example, $\alpha^2\beta^5\gamma^5\delta^7 = (\alpha\beta\gamma\delta)^2(\beta\gamma\delta)^3\delta^2$.

Let the elementary symmetric functions to which these groupings of the n arguments belong be e_n, e_{n-1}, etc. Then T is a term in the expansion of

$$E = e_n^r e_{n-1}^{s-r}\ldots$$

in terms of the arguments α, β, ..., λ.

For example, $\alpha^2\beta^5\gamma^5\delta^7$ is a term in

$$e_4^2e_3^3e_2^0e_1^2 = (\Sigma\alpha\beta\gamma\delta)^2(\Sigma\alpha\beta\gamma)^3(\Sigma\alpha)^2.$$

But since E is a symmetric function it too may be expressed monomially in lexical order

$$E = c_1'E_1 + c_2'E_2 + \dots + c_k'E_k,$$

where E_1 is necessarily the monomial due to the set of indices $\{rs\dots t\}$. (In the example E_1 consists of terms of indices 2, 5, 5, 7 only.) Hence $E_1 = S_1$ and $c_1' \neq 0$. On dividing by the non-zero constant c_1' we express E_1 or S_1 rationally and integrally in terms of E and earlier monomials $E_2, E_3, \dots, E_k$ for which the theorem has been assumed true. Since E is itself in the required form this proves the theorem by induction. The reduction is unique (p. 148).

34. Further Theory of Symmetric Functions. Taking the case of the third order, let

$$e_1 = \alpha+\beta+\gamma, \quad e_2 = \beta\gamma+\gamma\alpha+\alpha\beta, \quad e_3 = \alpha\beta\gamma,$$

so that α, β, γ are the roots of the cubic

$$x^3 = e_1x^2 - e_2x + e_3.$$

Multiply this by x and substitute for x^3 in terms of lower powers: then

$$\begin{aligned} x^4 &= e_1x^3 - e_2x^2 + e_3x \\ &= (e_1^2 - e_2)x^2 - (e_1e_2 - e_3)x + e_1e_3. \end{aligned}$$

Similarly, x^5 is expressible in terms of x^3, x^2, x and therefore of x^2, x^1, x^0; and so on. We infer that, if $x = \alpha$ or β or γ, we can always express a power of x as a quadratic

$$x^k = E_1x^2 + E_2x + E_3, \quad x = \alpha, \beta, \gamma, \qquad (1)$$

where E_1, E_2, E_3 are polynomials in e_1, e_2, e_3 with integral coefficients.

Now take any three positive integers l, m, n and form the determinant

$$\Delta = |\,\alpha^l\beta^m\gamma^n\,| = \begin{vmatrix} \alpha^l & \beta^l & \gamma^l \\ \alpha^m & \beta^m & \gamma^m \\ \alpha^n & \beta^n & \gamma^n \end{vmatrix}.$$

We can therefore write this as

$$\varDelta = \begin{vmatrix} E_1\alpha^2+E_2\alpha+E_3 & E_1\beta^2+E_2\beta+E_3 & E_1\gamma^2+E_2\gamma+E_3 \\ F_1\alpha^2+F_2\alpha+F_3 & F_1\beta^2+F_2\beta+F_3 & F_1\gamma^2+F_2\gamma+F_3 \\ G_1\alpha^2+G_2\alpha+G_3 & G_1\beta^2+G_2\beta+G_3 & G_1\gamma^2+G_2\gamma+G_3 \end{vmatrix}$$

$$= \begin{vmatrix} E_1 & E_2 & E_3 \\ F_1 & F_2 & F_3 \\ G_1 & G_2 & G_3 \end{vmatrix} \begin{vmatrix} \alpha^2 & \beta^2 & \gamma^2 \\ \alpha & \beta & \gamma \\ 1 & 1 & 1 \end{vmatrix} = \varDelta(e)\varDelta(\alpha\beta\gamma),$$

let us say, by the multiplication theorem of determinants (Aitken, *Determinants and Matrices*, p. 80), where the nine quantities E, F, G are polynomials in e_1, e_2, e_3 with integer coefficients, and hence $\varDelta(e)$ is so too.

If α, β, γ all differ the cofactor determinant $|\alpha^2\beta^1\gamma^0|$ is the difference-product $(\alpha-\beta)(\alpha-\gamma)(\beta-\gamma)$, and the quotient

$$|\alpha^l\beta^m\gamma^n| \div |\alpha^2\beta^1\gamma^0|$$

is identically equal to $\varDelta(e)$ which is a symmetric function of α, β, γ. We call this quotient a bialternant (*Ibid.*, p. 113) of order three. Exactly similar treatment applies to any number of roots α, β, ..., λ. A bialternant is characterized by its arguments α, β, γ, ... and its positive integral indices l, m, n, ... Thus

Every bialternant is expressible as a polynomial in the elementary symmetric functions e_i *with integer coefficients.*

Next, a function $\phi(\alpha, \beta, \gamma)$ which changes sign whenever any two of its arguments α, β, γ are interchanged is called an *alternating function* of its arguments; and similarly for any number of arguments. For instance,

$$\phi(\alpha, \beta, \gamma) = -\phi(\beta, \alpha, \gamma) = \phi(\beta, \gamma, \alpha) = \text{etc.}$$

Hence the square of an alternating function is a symmetric function; so also is the product or the quotient of two alternating functions. But if $\psi(\alpha, \beta, \gamma)$ is symmetric, the product $\phi\psi$ alternates; in fact

$$\phi(\alpha, \beta, \gamma)\ \psi(\alpha, \beta, \gamma) = -\phi(\beta, \alpha, \gamma)\ \psi(\beta, \alpha, \gamma).$$

The alternant $|\alpha^2\beta^1\gamma^0|$ is an alternating function, and so is the more general $|\alpha^l\beta^m\gamma^n|$. Their quotient, which is a bialternant, is then symmetric.

Alternative Proof of the Fundamental Theorem for Symmetric Functions. The above considerations lead to a notable proof of the theorem that every monomial symmetric function of α, β, γ, ... is a polynomial, with integer coefficients, in e_1, e_2, e_3, ...

For let $\Sigma\alpha^p\beta^q\gamma^r = \psi$ be such a monomial symmetric function. Multiply it by

$$\phi \equiv |\alpha^2\beta^1\gamma^0| = \Sigma\pm\alpha^2\beta^1\gamma^0.$$

Then $\phi\psi = \Sigma\pm\alpha^{p+2}\beta^{q+1}\gamma^r + \Sigma\pm\alpha^{q+2}\beta^{p+1}\gamma^r + \ldots,$

where the whole summation extends to six terms due to permuting α, β, γ among themselves, and again to terms due to permuting p, q, r. Hence

$$\phi\psi = |\alpha^{p+2}\beta^{q+1}\gamma^r| + |\alpha^{q+2}\beta^{p+1}\gamma^r| + \ldots .$$

Divide throughout by $\phi = |\alpha^2\beta^1\gamma^0|$, and this at once expresses ψ as a sum of bialternants such as

$$|\alpha^{p+2}\beta^{q+1}\gamma^r|/|\alpha^2\beta^1\gamma^0|,$$

each of which we have seen to be equal to a polynomial in the elementary symmetric functions e and with integer coefficients.

The above method is general and applicable to n variables α. If $\psi = \Sigma\alpha^p\beta^q\gamma^r\ldots\lambda^s$ is a monomial symmetric function where $p+q+r+\ldots+s = n$ and some of the indices may be zero, the number of terms in this summation is the number of distinct permutations of the n letters p, q, ..., s taken all at a time.

An Alternative Based on Cauchy's Proof. Let us segregate one root α and let $e_1 = \alpha+f_1$, $e_2 = \alpha f_1+f_2$, $e_3 = \alpha f_2+f_3$, ..., $e_n = \alpha f_{n-1}$, so that the expressions

$$f_1 = \beta+\gamma+\ldots,\ f_2 = \beta\gamma+\beta\delta+\ldots,\ \ldots,\ f_{n-1} = \beta\gamma\ldots\lambda$$

are the elementary symmetric functions of the $n-1$ remaining roots. If ψ is a monomial symmetric function of the n roots, arrange it as

$$\psi_0+\alpha\psi_1+\alpha^2\psi_2+\dots,$$

where each ψ_i is a function of the $n-1$ roots, in which it is necessarily symmetric. Assume the theorem true for these $n-1$ roots, so that each ψ is expressible as a function of the f_i. But

$$f_1 = e_1-\alpha,\ f_2 = e_2-\alpha f_1 = e_2-\alpha e_1+\alpha^2, \text{ and so on.}$$

Hence each ψ is also a polynomial function of the e_i and of α ; let us say finally that

$$\psi = E_0+E_1\alpha+E_2\alpha^2+\dots+E_{n-1}\alpha^{n-1},$$

where each E is a polynomial in the e_i, and by (1) p. 77 no power α^p higher than α^{n-1} is needed.

By symmetry exactly the same equation is satisfied by $\beta, \gamma, \dots, \lambda$, so that

$$\psi = E_0+E_1\beta+E_2\beta^2+\dots+E_{n-1}\beta^{n-1}, \text{ etc.}$$

Either all of $E_0-\psi$, E_1, E_2, ..., E_{n-1} vanish, or else by elimination $|\alpha^1\beta^1\gamma^2\dots\lambda^n| = 0$, which cannot be true since this determinant is equal to the difference-product of arguments α, β, ..., λ all different. Hence $\psi = E_0$ and all the other E_i vanish. This expresses ψ as a polynomial in the e_i, and the rest follows by induction.

Examples :

1. Evaluate s_3, s_5, s_7 for $x^3-5x+1=0$.
2. Evaluate $\Sigma\alpha^{-3}$ for $4x^4-12x^3+5x^2-3x+1=0$.
3. Prove that

$$\begin{vmatrix} s_0 & s_1 & s_2 & s_3 \\ s_1 & s_2 & s_3 & s_4 \\ s_2 & s_3 & s_4 & s_5 \\ s_3 & s_4 & s_5 & s_6 \end{vmatrix} = \begin{vmatrix} 1 & 1 & 1 & 1 \\ \alpha & \beta & \gamma & \delta \\ \alpha^2 & \beta^2 & \gamma^2 & \delta^2 \\ \alpha^3 & \beta^3 & \gamma^3 & \delta^3 \end{vmatrix}^2 .$$

CHAPTER VI

TRANSFORMATION AND NUMERICAL SOLUTION OF ALGEBRAIC EQUATIONS

35. Increasing or Decreasing all the Roots of an Equation by the Same Amount. Given an equation

$$f(x) = a_0x^n + a_1x^{n-1} + \ldots + a_{n-1}x + a_n = 0 \quad . \quad (1)$$

we shall seek for the equation

$$F(y) = b_0y^n + b_1y^{n-1} + \ldots + b_{n-1}y + b_n = 0 \quad . \quad (2)$$

each of whose roots is h less than the corresponding root of $f(x) = 0$. In other words, we transform $f(x)$ to $F(y)$ by taking

$$x = y + h.$$

In the factorized form we shall then have

$$\begin{aligned} f(x) &= a_0(x-\alpha)(x-\beta)\ldots(x-\lambda) \\ &= a_0(y+h-\alpha)(y+h-\beta)\ldots(y+h-\lambda) \\ &= F(y). \end{aligned}$$

The roots of the equation $F(y) = 0$ are clearly $\alpha - h$, $\beta - h$, and so on, and these are of the required form ; and so we have found the required polynomial $F(y)$, only in factorized shape. Without yet knowing the roots for x we can obtain $F(y)$ directly by writing

$$f(x) = a_0(y+h)^n + a_1(y+h)^{n-1} \ldots + a_n, \quad . \quad . \quad (3)$$

expanding each term and then rearranging. In practice this is done by Horner's method (**16**) p. 32.

Examples. 1. To reduce each root of

$$x^4-2x^3+3x-4=0 \text{ by } 3.$$

$$\begin{array}{cccccl}
1 & -2 & 0 & 3 & -4 & (3 \\
 & 3 & 3 & 9 & 36 & \\
\hline
 & 1 & 3 & 12 & 32 & \\
 & 3 & 12 & 45 & & \\
\hline
 & 4 & 15 & 57 & & \\
 & 3 & 21 & & & \\
\hline
 & 7 & 36 & & & \qquad x = y+3, \\
 & 3 & & & & \\
\hline
 & 10 & & & &
\end{array}$$

$$y^4+10y^3+36y^2+57y+32 = 0.$$

2. Increase the roots of $x^4+4x^3-19x^2-106x-120 = 0$ by 3. Hence solve the equation: $(y^4-8y^3-y^2+8y = 0)$.

3. Decrease the roots of $x^3+2x-2 = 0$ by 0·7.

$$(y^3+2{\cdot}1y^2+3{\cdot}47y-0{\cdot}257 = 0).$$

36. Removal of the Second or Third Term of an Equation. If the relation **35** (3) is expanded, the coefficients of y^n and the next two highest powers of y are respectively

$$a_0, \quad na_0h+a_1, \quad \tfrac{1}{2}n(n-1)a_0h^2+(n-1)a_1h+a_2 \quad . \qquad (1)$$

If we choose $h = -a_1/na_0$ the second term in the resulting equation for y disappears. If instead we choose h to make the quadratic expression in n, the coefficient of y^{n-2}, vanish, then the third term of the equation for y disappears. Usually the same value of h fails to make both terms disappear and we content ourselves with the first step only. Since a_1/na_0 is rational the step is readily taken, and the resulting equation is manifestly simpler than the original.

Examples. Remove the second term from the equations

$x^3+6x^2-7x-4=0$, $2x^3+x^2-1=0$, $x^4-8x^3+x^2-x+3=0$. (Here $h=-2$, $-\frac{1}{6}$, 2; $y^3-19y+26=0$, $2y^3-\frac{1}{6}y-\frac{53}{54}=0$, $y^4-23y^2-61y-43=0$).

Increasing or Decreasing all the Roots by a Constant Multiple. Let $x=ky$; then

$$f(x)=a_0k^ny^n+a_1k^{n-1}y^{n-1}+\ldots+a_n=0.$$

This is of special numerical use when k is a power of 10. For example, we can regard the equations

$$x^3+2{\cdot}1x^2+3{\cdot}47x-0{\cdot}257=0,$$
$$x^3+21x^2+347x-257=0,$$
$$x^3+0{\cdot}21x^2+0{\cdot}0347x-0{\cdot}000257=0$$

as essentially the same. If the roots of the first are α, β, γ those of the second are 10α, 10β, 10γ, and of the third are $\alpha/10$, $\beta/10$, $\gamma/10$.

37. Horner's Method of Solving an Equation. An equation may always be solved to any desired degree of approximation, as far as its real roots are concerned, by Horner's method. This is best explained by an actual example: we shall take $f(x)=x^3-4x^2+6x-18984=0$.

Here $f(0)$ is negative, so that the graph of $f(x)$ crosses the axis $x=0$ below the origin, but $f(100)$ is positive, and the graph crosses the parallel $x=100$ above the axis $y=0$. Since the graph is continuous it must cut $y=0$ at least once between $x=0$ and $x=100$. By trial we find that $f(20)<0$, $f(30)>0$, so that a root lies between 20 and 30. Now reduce all roots by 20. This gives an equation $y^3+56y^2+1046y=12464$ which must therefore have a real root between 0 and 10. Reduce the roots by 8. (The choice of 8 will be explained presently.) The new equation is $z^3+80z^2+2134z=0$, where the balance in the final column of the Horner scheme is zero. Accordingly $z = 0$ solves it : and $x = 20+8 = 28$.

1	−4	6	−18984 (28
	20	320	6520
	16	326	−12464
	20	720	12464
	36	1046	0
	20	512	
	56	1558	
	8	576	
	64	2134	
	8		
	72		
	8		
	80		

$$0 = z = y-8 = x-28.$$

The actual equation for z is $z^3+80z^2+2134z = 0$, which shows that $z = 0$, or else must be complex since $80^2 < 4(2134)$. So the roots for x, being 28 greater than for z, are 28 itself and two complex values also.

How, it will be asked, was the figure 8 chosen for the reduction of y? Had 9 been chosen the balance in the third column would have been increased by more than 512 and that of the fourth would have become positive. This last fact shows that $f(20+9)>0$ and therefore 29 is too large a number. Also 7 would have been too small, for, except at the initial step, we always choose the highest digit which will reduce the numerical balance in the last column as much as possible *without changing its original sign*, from − to + or from + to −.

Notice that in the working arrangement, as exemplified above, the successive reductions can be carried out as successive continuations of the first one.

More often than not the root is a non-terminating decimal. In such a case the balance in the final column is never zero. The following worked example is chosen for comparison with the preceding.

Example. Solve $x^3-4x^2+6x-20{,}000 = 0$.

1	−4	6	−20000 (28·4
	20	320	6520
	16	326	−13480
	20	720	12464
	36	1046	−1016·000
	20	512	866·464
	56	1558	−149·536
	8	576	
	64	2134·00	
	8	32·16	
	72	2166·16	
	8	32·32	
	80·0	2198·48	
	0·4		
	80·4		
	0·4		
	80·8		
	0·4		
	81·2		

The method is the same as before, but at the third stage a reduction of the root by 0·4 is effected (trial shows that 0·5 is too large: it would make a positive final balance). Since the operation is persistently that of adding 0·4 times the balance, it is hardly surprising to note that the balances in the second and third columns are altering relatively little. The change is less at each successive stage: at the next, with 0·06, we should have

81·20	2198·4800	−149·536000 (0·06
0·06	4·8756	132·201336
81·26	2203·3556	−17·334664
0·06	4·8792	
81·32	2208·2348	
0·06		
81·38		

This leaves a negative balance in the final column: 0·07 would have given a positive. The next approximation is 0·007 which adds on less than 0·6 in the third column. The fourth decimal figure in the answer would add on even less, but the number of significant digits in the balances is becoming unwieldy. Let us therefore redress the balances by deleting digits from the right—one from the last column but one, two from the last but two, three from the last but three, and so on. We then have

81·~~38~~	2208·234~~8~~	−17·334664	(0·007847745
	0·569	15·461628	
	2208·804	−1·873036	
	0·569	1·767544	
~~81~~	2209·37~~3~~	−0·105492	
	0·06	88380	
	2209·43	−0·017112	
	0·06	15466	
	2~~209~~·~~49~~	1646	
		1547	
		99	
		88	
		11	
		11	
		0	

$$x = 28{\cdot}467847745\ldots.$$

Considering the precision of the result, which gives x to ten significant figures, the labour involved is by no means unreasonable. We may note a few general principles:

(i) After the first and perhaps the second digit has been found the remaining figures are successively given with comparative ease. Each new figure is roughly given on dividing the balance in the final column by that in the next preceding column. (For example, the third significant figure 4 in the illustration above is suggested by 1016000/213400.) But we must allow for a possible increase in such a divisor; as in this case 213400 rises to 216616.

(ii) The decimal point may be omitted except in the answer. Instead, at each new stage the balances may be multiplied by 1, 10, 100, 1000 and so on, from left to right. Thus we attach one, two, three ciphers to the balance in columns two, three, four and treat them all as whole numbers. This is illustrated in the example which now follows.

Example. $x^3-0{\cdot}4x^2+0{\cdot}06x-20 = 0.$

1	−0·4	0·06	−20	(2·846785
	2	3·2	6·52	
	1·6	3·26	−13·48	
	2	7·2	−13480*	
	3·6	10·46	12464	
	2	1046	−1016000*	
	5·6	512	866464	
	*56	1558	−149536	
	8	576	132204	
	64	213400	−17332	
	8	3216	15456	
	72	216616	−1876	
	8	3232	1766	
	*800	21984~~8~~	−110	
	4	49	110	
	804	22034		
	4	49		
	808	22~~0~~~~8~~~~3~~		
	4			
	8~~1~~~~2~~			
	~~8~~			

(* As in (ii) above.)

(iii) Contraction may alternatively be employed, by deleting figures as already explained. It uses up the balances and produces a result to about twice as many significant figures as were reached at the stage when contraction began.

(iv) At the 7 of the third decimal place in x on p. 86 the balances were 1, 81·38, 2208·2348, etc. Contraction gave 81, 2208·234, but 569 was entered as the approximation better than $81\times 7=567$. It was obtained by paying attention to the figures 38 just deleted. Similarly, the deleted 8 in the third column contributed to the next balance 2208·804.

Again for comparison almost the same equation is dealt with on p. 87, but contraction takes place after three stages.

38. Rational Roots of an Equation. If the coefficients of an algebraic equation are complex we may replace the equation by one of higher degree whose coefficients are real and whose roots include all the original roots (**5**, Ex. 2, and **27**, p. 64). If these real coefficients are irrational we may approximate to them by decimals to any degree of accuracy, in which case the corresponding roots are approximations also of any degree of accuracy (p. 69). Multiplication by a suitable power of 10 then removes the decimals and yields integer coefficients. Hence the limitation of the discussion to rational equations, with integer coefficients, is less of a restriction than at first sight appears.

For example, $\sqrt{2}x^2-(\sqrt{3}+\frac{1}{2})x+4=0$

is approximately equivalent, with fair accuracy, to

$$1{\cdot}414x^2-2{\cdot}232x+4=0,$$

and with still more accuracy, to

$$1{\cdot}41421x^2-2{\cdot}23205x+4=0,$$

that is, to

$$141421x^2-223205x+400000=0.$$

Equations with Integer Coefficients. We may always reduce a given equation to the form

$$x^n+a_1x^{n-1}+a_2x^{n-2}+...+a_n = 0. \quad . \quad (1)$$

A case of special interest arises when the coefficients a_1, a_2, ..., a_n are all integers, for the roots of the equation are then (**6**) p. **11**, algebraic integers. If all the coefficients a_0, a_1, ..., a_n of an algebraic equation are integers the reduction to the still more special form (1), in which $a_0 = 1$, can always be carried out; for we have only to take $z = a_0x$ as a new variable to obtain an equation in z, namely,

$$z^n+a_0a_1z^{n-1}+a_0^2a_2z^{n-2}+...+a_0^na_n = 0,$$

which is evidently of the form (1).

For example, if $7x^2-6x-5 = 0$, and $z = 7x$, we have

$$49x^2-42x-35 = 0, \text{ that is, } z^2-6z-35 = 0.$$

Theorem. Each rational root of an equation with integer coefficients which is in the form (1) *above is necessarily an integer.*

Proof. Let p/q, rational and in its lowest terms, be a root of equation (1). Then

$$(p/q)^n+a_1(p/q)^{n-1}+...+a_n = 0. \quad . \quad . \quad (2)$$

Multiply through by q^{n-1}. Then every term is a whole number except the first, which is p^n/q, a fraction. This is impossible: hence p/q must be a whole number.

To Find the Rational Roots of a Rational Equation. If $a_0 \neq 1$ we first bring the equation to the standard form (1). By the factorized form of a polynomial (**25**) p. 60, a_n is now the product of the roots of the equation, and these if rational are integers, as we have just seen. Thus the only possible rational roots are to be found among the factors of a_n, with positive or negative sign affixed, and these must be examined one by one.

Example. $9x^4+6x^3+19x^2+6x-16 = 0.$

Instead of multiplying by 9^3 it is enough here to multiply throughout by 9 and to put $3x = z$. This gives

$$f(z) = z^4+2z^3+19z^2+18z-144 = 0.$$

The factors of 144 are ±1, ±2, ±3, ±4, ±6, ±8, ±9, ±12, etc. Actual roots are 2, -3, so that $(z-2)(z+3)$ is a factor of $f(z)$. The other factor is z^2+z+24, which leads to complex roots. Hence $x = \frac{2}{3}$, -1, and two complex values.

39. Other Methods of Solving Equations. Iteration. If the equation $f(x) = 0$ can be readily thrown into the form $x = \phi(x)$ it is sometimes possible to solve it by iteration. Geometrically the problem consists in finding the x coordinate of a point Z common to the line OP and the curve LM, whose equations are $y = x$, and $y = \phi(x)$ respectively.

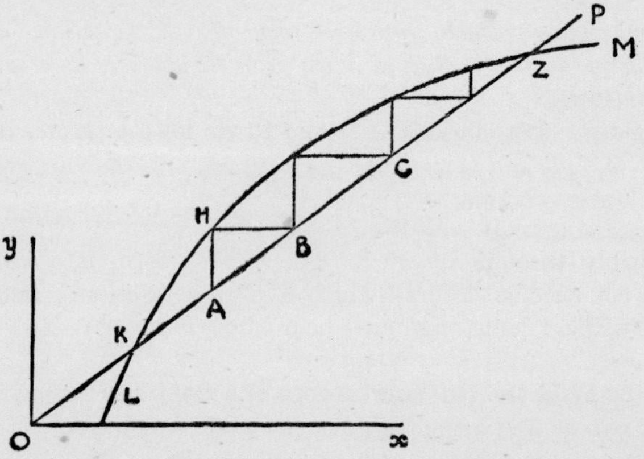

Take any point A on OP and draw a staircase or spiral polygon, with lines alternately parallel to Oy and Ox and corners alternately on the curve and on the line OP. In both figures the points A, B, C, ... tend to the desired limit Z, the point where OP cuts the curve LM.

Now the coordinates of B, C, ... are easily found from those of A. If A is (a, a), B is (b, b), etc., then evidently the ordinate y of B is that of H, the point $(a, \phi(a))$. Hence $b = \phi(a)$, $c = \phi(b)$, $d = \phi(c)$, ...

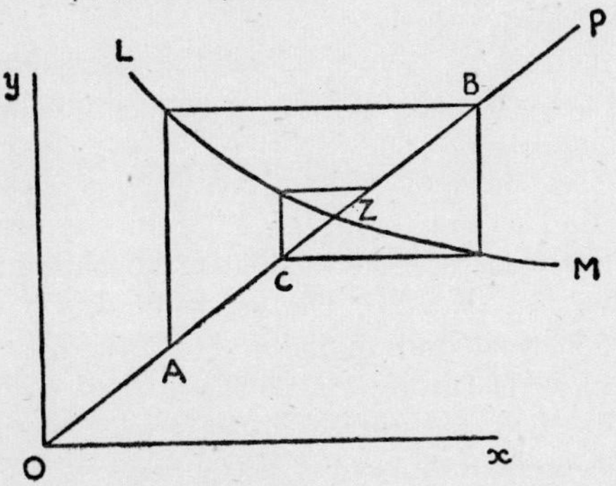

Whenever the sequence $a, b, c, d, \ldots$ tends to a limit α it furnishes a root α of the equation $f(x) = 0$.

Example. $$x^3 - 2x - 5 = 0.$$

Take this in the form $x = \sqrt[3]{(2x+5)}$ and let $a = 2$.

Then $b = \sqrt[3]{9} = 2{\cdot}08..$ and so $2b+5 = 9{\cdot}16..$

Thus $c = \sqrt[3]{9{\cdot}16} = 2{\cdot}092..$ and $2c+5 = 9{\cdot}184..$

$d = \sqrt[3]{9{\cdot}184} = 2{\cdot}0942..$, and in the same way

$e = 2{\cdot}0945..$, $f = 2{\cdot}09455..$

Actually $\alpha = 2{\cdot}09455148...$

The process is available whenever the repeated calculation of $\phi(x)$ can readily be effected. While the choice of the initial value a is largely arbitrary, it may quite possibly lead to a divergent sequence. For example, had A been taken to the left of the point K in Fig. 1 it would have led to a staircase diverging from K, as experiment will at once show. Unless the curve were to recross the line PK produced no limit would then be found.

Also in Fig. 2 if the curve at Z crosses OP at 45° downwards, that is, if $\phi'(a) = -1$ at $(a, \phi(a))$ then difficulties may arise. Indeed, if the arc LM is symmetrical with regard to OP, cutting OP at right angles, the spiral polygon becomes a square on diagonal AB, endlessly repeated: and C coincides with A.

The method of iteration has the agreeable property that it is not seriously vitiated by an intermediate mistake or two committed in the calculation at any stage, provided that the sequence of results points to a clear limiting value! Had c been taken as 2·082 in the example this would merely have been equivalent to choosing a value of a rather less than 2. The values of d, e, f would still have 2·09 as their leading digits.

This pleasing feature makes the method popular. For a more detailed account of it the reader should consult Whittaker and Robinson, *The Calculus of Observations*, pp. 78-84. The method is due to James Gregory and Michael Dary independently in 1674. The same principle was also used by Newton (1707).

40. The Approximate Method of Newton. If the curve $y = f(x)$ is known to cut Ox near a point $x = a$, we may proceed as follows: Choose a point A near to Z

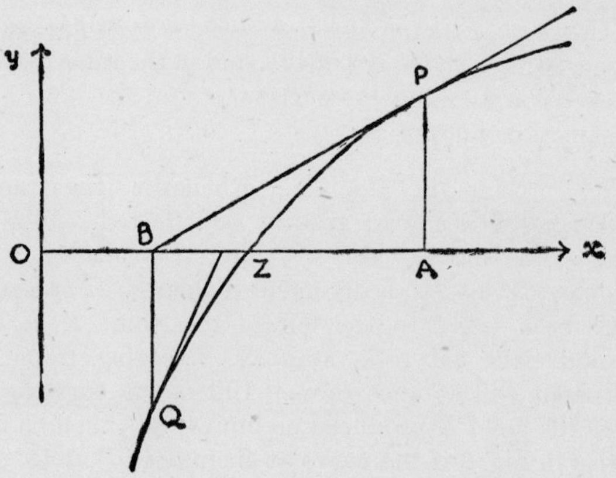

on the axis of x: draw the ordinate AP to cut the curve at P, and the tangent PB to cut Ox at B. Draw the ordinate BQ to cut the curve at Q and the tangent QC to cut OX at C. Repeat the process. If $y = f(x)$ denotes the curve and if both $f'(x)$ and $f''(x)$ do not vanish in the range AB in the first figure or AZ in the second, then this procedure, repeated again and again, yields points A, B, C, ... which approximate to the point Z, as the actual construction shows.

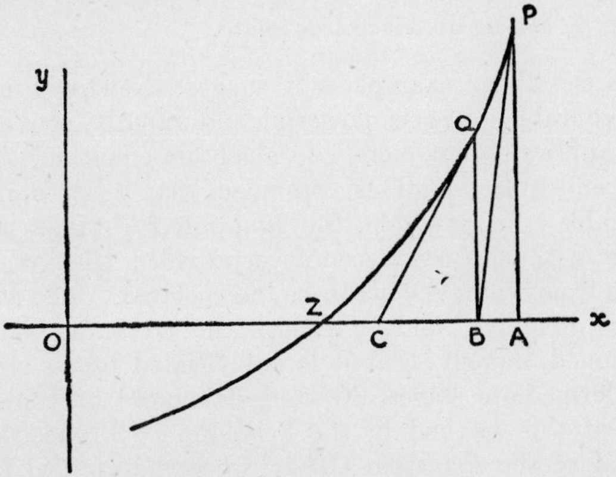

In this way we find a series of successive approximations to the root α of the equation $f(x) = 0$, which lies near a given value $x = a$.

Analytically, let $y - f(a) = f'(a)(x - a)$ be the equation of the tangent at P, the point $(a, f(a))$. Then OB or b is given by putting $y = 0$, so that

$$b = a - f(a)/f'(a).$$

Similarly, $c = b - f(b)/f'(b)$, and so on (see also p. 159).

Example. $x^3 - 2x - 5 = 0.$

Here $f(2) = -3, f(3) = 16$, so that a root lies between 2 and 3.

Put $a = 2$. Then $b = a - (a^3 - 2a - 5)/(3a^2 - 2) = 2{\cdot}1$.

Also
$$c = 2{\cdot}1 - \frac{2{\cdot}1^3-4{\cdot}2-5}{3\times 2{\cdot}1^2-2}$$
$$= 2{\cdot}1 - \frac{9{\cdot}261-9{\cdot}2}{13{\cdot}23-2} = 2{\cdot}0946.$$
$$d = 2{\cdot}0946 - \frac{2{\cdot}0946^3-4{\cdot}1892-5}{3\times 2{\cdot}0946^2-2}$$
$$= 2{\cdot}0946-0{\cdot}00054155/11{\cdot}162$$
$$= 2{\cdot}094551483,$$
where the last figure 3 is approximate.

As the above example may suggest, Newton's method in favourable cases is powerful and rapidly convergent. It is applicable not merely to algebraic equations, but to transcendental equations, provided that $f'(x)$ is readily calculable : for example, the equation $x = \tan x$ can be solved with sufficient accuracy, provided that we have tables from which $\sec^2 x$ can be interpolated. The method is also iterative, and so enjoys the advantage already mentioned, namely, that it is not vitiated by an error at an intermediate stage. Newton elaborated a geometrical form of this method in the Scholium of Proposition 31 Book I of the *Principia* (1687), where he applied it first to the equation $x-e \sin x = N$, and next to $e \sinh x-x = N$. These equations arose out of Kepler's Problem, to find the position of a planet at a given time in an elliptic or hyperbolic orbit of eccentricity e.

Examples.

1. Show that $e^x-1 = 2x$ has one positive real root, and approximate to it by Newton's method. [Take $a = 1$.] Then $b = 1{\cdot}392$, $c = 1{\cdot}275$, $d = 1{\cdot}256$.

2. Determine the real roots of $x^5-10x^3+4 = 0$ to two significant figures.

Horner's method leads to the values $-3{\cdot}182034$, $0{\cdot}751234$, $3{\cdot}141818$. Newton's method, with $a = 1$, $b = {\cdot}8$, $c = 0{\cdot}7538$ roughly approximates to the smaller positive root.

CHAPTER VII

THE LOCATION OF THE ROOTS OF AN EQUATION

41. The Significance of the Sign of a Polynomial. Let us consider the graph of the real polynomial

$$y = a_0x^n + a_1x^{n-1} + \ldots + a_n \equiv f(x).$$

It is a continuous line which crosses each line parallel to the axis $x = 0$ once, and it crosses the axis $y = 0$, or touches it, at those values of x which give the roots of the equation $f(x) = 0$. If $f(a) < 0$ and $f(b) > 0$ we say that y, or $f(x)$, changes sign as x passes from a to b. Now y is negative at $x = a$, changes continuously in value as x changes, and becomes positive when $x = b$. Unless y vanishes for some value of x between a and b this could not happen. Hence there is a root between $x = a$ and $x = b$. Similar reasoning applies if $f(a) > 0$ and $f(b) < 0$.

Now consider the graph itself with its possible ups and downs. Let A be the point on the graph where $x = a$, and B be the point where $x = b$.

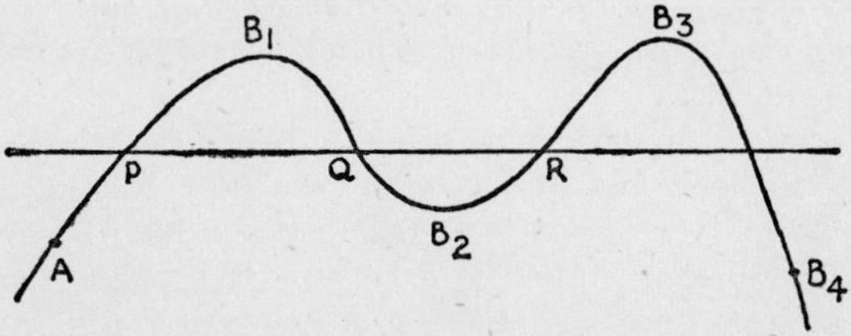

If $f(a) < 0$, $f(b) > 0$ there may be one real root between A and B (as when B is at B_1 in the figure) : or three real roots (as when B is at B_3 in the figure), but certainly not two real roots, or four real roots.

If the graph touches the axis $y = 0$ we can regard the point of contact as the point of coincidence of two roots of the equation.

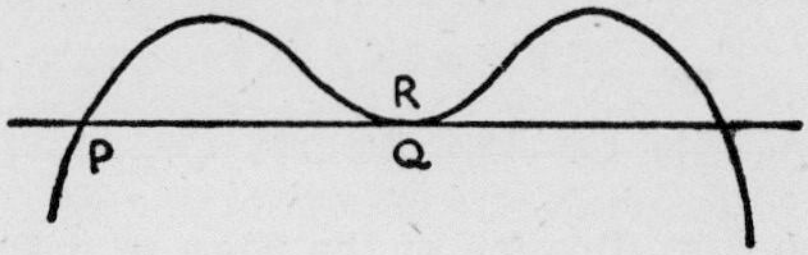

If the graph touches the axis $y = 0$ at an inflexion, we can regard the point of inflexion as the point of

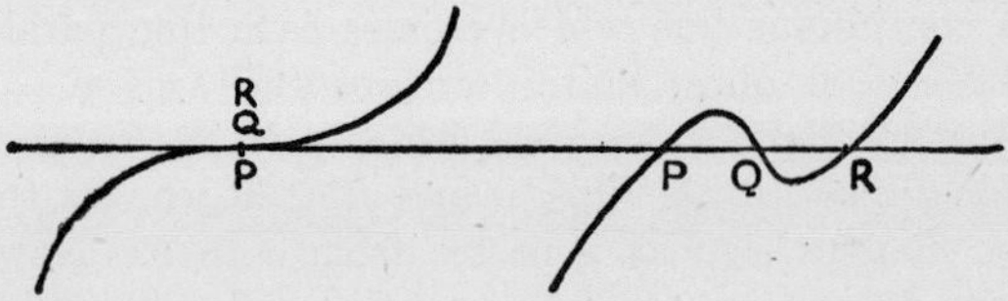

coincidence of three roots of the equation. And so on. The characteristic property is therefore as follows :

Theorem. An odd number or an even number of real roots of an equation f(x) = 0 *lie between two values* x = a *and* x = b, *according as* f(a), f(b) *differ in sign or have the same sign.*

Corollary. An equation of odd degree must have at least one real root ; and equation of even degree need not necessarily have a real root.

For if x is large $f(x)$ behaves like a_0x^n (*cf.* p. 21), where without loss of generality we may take $a_0 = 1$. If $x<0$ so is x^n when n is odd. We write $f(-\infty)<0$. And if $x>0$ so is x^n, and so $f(\infty)>0$. Hence $f(x)$ changes sign at least once, and there is a real root. But if n is even $f(-\infty)$ and $f(+\infty)$ are both positive and the function $f(x)$ may indeed never become negative.

Examples. x^2+4, x^4+2x^2+4 are functions that cannot be negative for any real values of x.

42. Upper Bound to the Real Roots, and Newton's Rule. Let us take the equation with $a_0 = 1$, so that for large enough values of x the function $f(x)$ is positive. If b is such that $f(x)>0$ whenever $x>b$ we call b an *upper bound* (it used to be called an *upper limit*) to the real roots of the equation $f(x) = 0$. Manifestly it is a help, in the search for the roots, to ascertain that they are confined below such a definite value b. Obviously no root can exceed b, a value of x from which onwards $f(x)$ is always positive. There may also be numbers less than b which may yet exceed each root of $f(x) = 0$; the bounds may be drawn more tightly.

Newton gave a rule to the following effect: *if* f(b), f′(b), f″(b), ..., $\mathrm{f}^{(n)}(\mathrm{b})$ *are all positive,* b *is such an upper bound to the real roots of the equation* f(x) = 0.

The rule follows at once from Taylor's formula

$$f(x) = f(b+x-b) = f(b)+(x-b)f'(b)+\ldots+\frac{(x-b)^n}{n\,!}f^{(n)}(b),$$

since the right-hand expression is positive when $f(b)$ and its n successive derivatives are positive, and $x>b$; so that $f(x)>0$ whenever $x>b$.

Such a bound b is of course not unique, for any point to the right of b on the axis of x would answer equally well.

Examples.

1. $$f(x) = x^3-9x^2+4x+90 = 0,$$
$$f'(x) = 3x^2-18x+4,\ f''(x) = 6x-18.$$

Here $f''(x)>0$ if $x>3$ and $f'(x)<0$ at $x = 3, 4, 5$, but $f'(6)>0, f(6)>0$; hence no real root exceeds 6, which is an upper bound.

2. For $x^3-12x^2+57x-94 = 0,\ b = 4$.

Lower Bound to the Real Roots. The equation $x^nf(x^{-1}) = 0$, which reverses the given equation, has for its roots the reciprocals α^{-1}, β^{-1}, ..., λ^{-1} of the roots α, β, ..., λ of $f(x) = 0$. For

$$\begin{aligned} x^n f(x^{-1}) &= x^n(a_0 x^{-n} + a_1 x^{-n+1} + \ldots + a_n) \\ &= a_0 + a_1 x + \ldots + a_n x^n \\ &= a_0(1-\alpha x)(1-\beta x)\ldots(1-\lambda x), \quad . \quad . \quad (1) \end{aligned}$$

and the roots are α^{-1}, β^{-1}, ..., λ^{-1}. Now if no root lies between b and $+\infty$, when b is positive, then no reciprocal lies between b^{-1} and zero. Accordingly, if b is a positive upper bound of the reciprocal equation, b^{-1} is a lower bound for the positive roots of the original equation.

Example 3. The reciprocal equation to $f(x) = 0$ in Ex. 1 is $$90x^3 + 4x^2 - 9x + 1 = 0,$$
and the derivatives are

$$270x^2 + 8x - 9 \text{ and } 540x + 8.$$

Now $x = 1/5$ renders these three polynomials positive, and so no root lies between $1/5$ and $+\infty$, so that no root of the original equation lies between 5 and 0. We infer from Examples 1 and 3 that real positive roots of

$$x^3 - 9x^2 + 4x + 90 = 0$$

can only lie between $x = 5$ and $x = 6$.

A lower bound to all the real roots can be found by considering the upper bound of $f(-x) = 0$, the roots of which are $-\alpha$, $-\beta$, ..., $-\lambda$; and, finally, an upper bound to the negative roots is given by considering $x^n f(-x^{-1}) = 0$, the roots of which are $-\alpha^{-1}$, $-\beta^{-1}$, ..., $-\lambda^{-1}$.

Example 4. If $\phi(x) = x^3 + 9x^2 + 4x - 90 = 0$, then $\phi(-x) = 0$ is the equation of Ex. 1. The derivatives are positive for $x > 0$, but $\phi(0) < 0$, $\phi(2) < 0$, $\phi(3) > 0$. Hence $x = 3$ is an upper bound; and no root of the original equation of Ex. 1 is less than -3.

Again, when $f(a) < 0$, $f(b) > 0$, and $f'(x) > 0$ for $a < x < b$, then $f(x) = 0$ has exactly one root between a and b; for the graph must be climbing all the way between $x = a$ and $x = b$. In Ex. 4 there is exactly one root between 0 and 3.

43. Relative Location of Roots of an Equation and of the Derived Equation. The following important and useful theorem, first published by Rolle in 1689, is true for functions more general than polynomials, but is applied here to algebraic equations.

Rolle's Theorem. Between any two consecutive roots of the algebraic equation $\mathrm{f}(\mathrm{x}) = 0$ *there lie an odd number of roots of the equation* $\mathrm{f}'(\mathrm{x}) = 0$.

Since the graph $y = f(x)$ is continuous, $f(x)$ must have a maximum or minimum at least once between any two

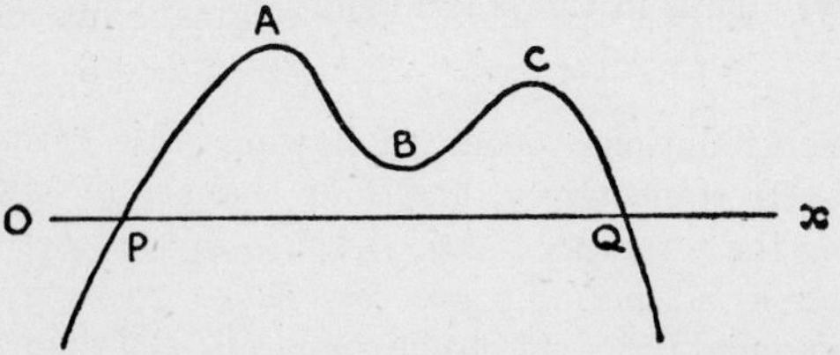

values $x = a$ and $x = \beta$ for which $f(x)$ vanishes. In fact $f(x)$ cannot always increase as x changes from a to β, if $f(a) = f(\beta)$: nor can it always decrease. Again, at such a maximum or minimum the gradient of the tangent is continuous, so that $f'(x)$ exists but is neither >0 nor <0. It can only be zero.

Once more, if an even number of zeros of $f'(x)$ lie between two points P and Q on the curve, then the gradients of the tangent at P and Q are both positive or both negative. Therefore if the curve is ascending through P it is ascending through Q: and this is impossible when P and Q lie at consecutive roots of the equation $f(x) = 0$. Similarly for descending values. Hence $f'(x)$ vanishes an odd number of times between two consecutive roots of $f(x) = 0$.

Corollary. The roots of $\mathrm{f}''(\mathrm{x}) = 0$ *separate those of* $\mathrm{f}'(\mathrm{x}) = 0$ *in a similar manner.*

For an illustration see p. 19, Ex. 1.

44. The Harriot–Descartes Rule of Signs. We now

proceed to investigate a remarkable theorem, implicit in the work of Harriot but first used explicitly by Descartes (1637), which limits the number of positive or negative roots of an equation ; but first we require some preliminary definitions.

When a polynomial $a_0x^n+a_1x^m+a_2x^p+\ldots+a_rx^q$ is arranged in descending order of index and has non-zero real coefficients, a *continuation* is said to occur whenever the signs of two consecutive terms are the same, and a *change* is said to occur whenever these two signs are contrary. Thus in the polynomial

$$x^8-3x^7+4x^5-x^4-2x^3-3x^2+2x+3$$

three continuations occur, following the terms $-x^4$, $-2x^3$, $+2x$ respectively, and four changes of sign occur, following the terms x^8, $-3x^7$, $+4x^5$, $-3x^2$ respectively.

When $n, m, p, \ldots, q$ are *consecutive* positive integers the polynomial $f(x)$ is said to be *complete*. All these remarks apply also to the associated equation $f(x)=0$. The theorem in question exhibits a connexion between these changes of sign and the number of positive roots of the equation. We begin with the following lemma:

Lemma. If a real polynomial, complete or incomplete, is multiplied by x−a, *where* a>0, *the product will contain at least one more change of sign than the original.*

(i) *Proof* for the complete polynomial. Let the multiplication be performed in the ordinary way, but let the signs only of the terms be written down ; then we shall have a scheme such as

$$\begin{array}{ccccccccccccc}
+ & + & + & - & - & + & - & - & + & + & - & + & \\
+ & - & & & & & & & & & & & \\
\hline
+ & + & + & - & - & + & - & - & + & + & - & + & \\
 & - & - & - & + & + & - & + & + & - & - & + & - \\
\hline
+ & \pm & \pm & - & \mp & + & - & \mp & + & \pm & - & + & -
\end{array}$$

The top row represents the complete polynomial written in descending order, wherein any arbitrary sequence of signs may occur. The second row represents $x-a$, where the signs are fixed as $+\ -$. A double sign is placed where the sign of any term in the product is ambiguous. The following laws will be seen by inspection to hold :—

(1) To every group of consecutive continuations in the original there corresponds a group of the same number of ambiguities in the product polynomial.

(2) In the product polynomial the signs before and after an ambiguity or group of consecutive ambiguities are contrary.

(3) In the product polynomial an extra term appears at the end, and with it a change of sign is introduced.

Now in the product polynomial take the most unfavourable case and suppose that all the ambiguities are replaced by continuations; then, by the second law, without affecting the number of continuations, the upper signs may be adopted for the ambiguities; and thus the signs of the original polynomial will be repeated in the product polynomial, except that by the third law there is an additional change of sign introduced at the end of the new polynomial. Thus in the most unfavourable case one more change of sign occurs in the product polynomial.

(ii) *Proof* for the incomplete polynomial. Introduce zeros, together with the signs $+$ and $-$, in the multiplication scheme, in order to indicate exactly the missing terms: for example,

$$\begin{array}{ccccccccccccccc} + & + & 0 & - & + & 0 & 0 & + & - & 0 & - & + & - & 0 & + \\ & - & - & 0 & + & - & 0 & 0 & - & + & 0 & + & - & + & 0 & - \end{array}$$

Between each zero, or group of zeros, is a complete subset of terms to which the preceding case applies, so that each subset gains at least one change of sign. But there may be a loss of a change at the actual gap, as in the first zero gap of the illustration above, where $+0-$

becomes $--$. Now the number of complete subsets separated by zero gaps is one more than the number of these gaps: hence the certain gains outweigh the possible losses by at least one. The result is thus established.

Descartes' Theorem. In any equation, complete or incomplete, the number of positive roots cannot exceed the number of changes of signs of the coefficients, and in any complete equation the number of negative roots cannot exceed the number of continuations in the signs of the coefficients.

Proof. Resolve $f(x)$ into $\psi(x)(x-a)(x-b)\ldots(x-c)$, where $\psi(x)$ contains all the factors due to negative and to pairs of complex roots, while all the factors $x-a$, and so on, due to positive roots are explicitly given. Now multiply $\psi(x)$ by $x-a$, $x-b$, ... in turn. At each multiplication at least one change of sign, by the lemma, is introduced into the product, so that the first part of the theorem follows immediately.

To prove the second part we suppose $f(x)$ to be complete and put $-y$ for x; then the original continuations of sign become changes of sign. Also the transformed equation cannot have more positive roots than it has changes; and thus there cannot be more negative roots in the original complete equation than the number of its continuations of sign.

Corollary. An equation, complete or incomplete, cannot have more negative roots than $f(-x)$ *has changes of sign.*

For the negative roots of $f(x) = 0$ are the same as the positive roots of $f(-x) = 0$.

Examples.

1. $x^3+2x-2 = 0$ has one change of sign and may therefore have one positive root. Actually it has a root between 0 and 1 since $f(1)>0>f(0)$. Now

$$(-x)^3+2(-x)-2 = 0$$

has no change of sign, and therefore has no positive root; and so the original equation has no negative root. It has two complex roots.

2. x^9-1 = has one real root, namely $x = 1$.
3. $x^{10}-1$ = has two real roots, namely $x = 1$, $x = -1$.
4. $x^3-2x^2-5 = 0$ has one real root, positive.
5. $x^4+x^2+1 = 0$ has no real root.

45. A Precise Rational Test for Real Roots. Remarkable as the Harriot-Descartes Rule of Signs is, it still leaves an uncertainty as to the *exact* number of real roots in an equation: it only gives an upper limit to them. The problem of finding an exact test engaged the attention of mathematicians for the next two hundred years, until it was finally solved in 1829 by Sturm, who published his result in the *Mémoires Divers des Savants Etrangers*, Paris, 1835. Sturm showed how to find for any equation, by rational methods, the exact number of real roots which lie within any given range of values.

Sturm's Theorem. There exists a set of real polynomials $f(x)$, $f'(x)$, $f_2(x)$, ..., $f_m(x)$ *whose degrees are in descending order, such that, if* $b>a$, *the number of distinct real roots of* $f(x) = 0$ *between* $x = a$ *and* $x = b$ *is equal to the excess of the number of changes of sign in the sequence* f, f', f_2, ..., f_m *when* $x = a$ *over the number of changes of sign when* $x = b$.

Proof. First suppose that $f(x)$ has no repeated factors. Take
$$f(x) = x^n+a_1x^{n-1}+\ldots+a_n,$$
$f'(x)$ its derivative, and $f_2(x)$ the remainder, with its sign changed, of the division $f(x)/f'(x)$. Continue the G.C.M. process until a constant is necessarily reached, since f and f' have no common factor (p. 61); but at each of the $m-1$ remainders change its sign before continuing. These modified remainders are the required functions f_i; and we have the following relations:

$$\begin{aligned} f &= q_1f' - f_2, \\ f' &= q_2f_2 - f_3, \\ &\ldots\ldots\ldots\ldots \\ f_{m-2} &= q_{m-1}f_{m-1} - f_m, \end{aligned}$$

where each f or q indicates a polynomial in x or, in the final case, a constant f_m.

From these relations we can draw certain inferences :

(1) $f_m \neq 0$, else all the preceding f's have a common factor involving x. Hence the constant f_m has a permanent sign $+$ or $-$, whatever value attaches to x.

(2) No two consecutive f's can vanish simultaneously ; else they and all their predecessors would have a common factor.

(3) If any $f_i = 0$ then, at this value of x, f_{i+1} and f_{i-1} have contrary signs, since they must be equal and opposite in value.

Now consider the sequence of signs in the set of f's when $x = a$, which is taken at a place where none of the f's vanish. As x increases from $x = a$ no change of sign within this sequence can occur until x reaches a zero of one of the f's. We therefore examine what happens at such a zero.

If $f_i = 0$ at $x = c$, take a range $\{c-h, c+h\}$ covering the value c, and such that no other f vanishes within the range. This is possible since the zeros of all the f's are definitely distinct. The signs of f_{i-1} at $x = c-h, c, c+h$ are the same, let us say $+ + +$: those of f_{i+1} are therefore $- - -$, by (3) above : while those of f_i are $\pm$, 0, $\pm$. Accordingly the signs of f_{i-1}, f_i, f_{i+1} are $+ \pm -$ just before, $+ 0 -$ at, and $+ \pm -$ just after $x = c$. In each case this group therefore presents one permanence and one change of sign as x passes through a zero of f_i ; and the same happens if f_{i-1} is negative at $x = c$.

This argument is equally valid for each f_i including f', but not for the initial member f of the sequence. As x increases and passes through an unrepeated root a of the equation $f = 0$, the signs of f must be either $+ 0 -$ or $- 0 +$, while the corresponding signs of f' must be $- - -$ or $+ + +$, according as f is decreasing or increasing through the root. In either case the signs of f, f' differ before, and are the same after, the passage of x through a; hence one change of sign is lost.

Thus we have proved that as x increases, Sturm's functions never lose a change of sign except when x passes through a root of the equation $f = 0$, and never gain a change of sign. Hence the number of changes of sign lost as x increases from a value $x = a$ to a greater value $x = b$ is equal to the number of the roots of the equation $f(x) = 0$ which lie between a and b. The theorem is thus established for the case of unrepeated factors.

Consider next the case where $f(x)$ has repeated factors. Then f, f' possess a G.C.M. $(x-\alpha)^p(x-\beta)^q \ldots = G$, which is common to all the Sturm functions f f', f_2, ..., f_m. Let us write $f = G\phi$, $f' = G\phi_1$, $f_2 = G\phi_2$, $f_m = G\phi_m$, where necessarily

$$\phi = (x-\alpha)(x-\beta) \ldots (x-\lambda)$$

and no two functions ϕ, ϕ_1, ϕ_2 ..., ϕ_m have a common factor. By the previous case the number of real zeros of ϕ can be ascertained from the Sturm sequence of ϕ's. At any value $x = c$ for which $G \neq 0$, the signs of the f's will be either identical with those of the ϕ's (for $G > 0$) or else will be entirely contrary (for $G < 0$). In either case the f sequence has the same number of changes of sign as the ϕ sequence. At a value $x = c$ for which $G = 0$, no signs appear at all, for all the f terms are zero. Hence the examination of the sequence of signs of the f series between $x = a$ and $x = b$ discovers the number of real roots of the equation $\phi = 0$, that is, the number of real distinct roots of $f = 0$, since every zero of f is included in ϕ. This completes the proof of the theorem.

Corollary 1. *If* f_r *is a remainder involving* x *and such that* f_r *remains positive, or remains negative, for all real values of* x *between* a *and* b, *then the sequence need not be prolonged beyond* f_r.

For in the preceding demonstration the necessary property of the last f was that it should never vanish, and as f_r cannot vanish the argument holds for the series $f, f', f_2, \ldots, f_r$.

Corollary 2. *Any* f *can be multiplied by a positive constant, or a factor involving* x, *provided that the factor remains positive throughout the range in question, and the modified function can be used for computing all further terms* f_i *of the sequence.*

For this modification leaves the essentials of the above proof unaltered.

Examples. 1. If $f(x) = x^3-3x^2-4x+13 = 0,$

$$f'(x) = 3x^2-6x-4,$$
$$f_2(x) = 2x-5,$$
$$f_3(x) = \tfrac{1}{2}.$$

The computation can be arranged as follows :

1	-3	-4	$+13$	3	-6	-4
3	-9	-12	$+39$	6	-12	-8
3	-6	-4		6	-15	
	-3	-8	$+39$		$+3$	-8
	-3	$+6$	$+4$		$+3$	$-7\frac{1}{2}$
	-7)	-14	$+35$			$-\frac{1}{2}$
		2	-5			

This is the ordinary G.C.M. process ; only after each remainder f_2 and f_3 the signs have been changed. To avoid fractions, f has been multiplied by 3 before the division. Division by -7 changes the sign of the first remainder and gives a suitable f_2, by Corollary 2. Next a scheme of signs can be devised :

	$f(x)$	$f'(x)$	$f_2(x)$	$f_3(x)$	Changes
$-\infty$	$-$	$+$	$-$	$+$	3
-10	$-$	$+$	$-$	$+$	3
0	$+$	$-$	$-$	$+$	2
1	$+$	$-$	$-$	$+$	2
2	$+$	$-$	$-$	$+$	2
3	$+$	$+$	$+$	$+$	0

In the first column we can write arbitrary values of x; in the last column we write down the number of changes of sign in the sequence. Here there is one negative root between -10 and zero, and two positive ones, between $x = 2$ and $x = 3$. Between which integers is the negative root?

2. If
$$f(x) = 2x^4 - 13x^2 + 10x - 49,$$
$$f'(x) = 2(4x^3 - 13x + 5),$$
$$f_2(x) = 13x^2 - 15x + 98.$$

Here f_2 has no real factors and is always positive for real values of x. The signs at $x = -\infty$ are $+-+$ and at $x = +\infty$ are $+++$; so that there are two real roots, as shown by two losses of change in sign. At $x = 0$, the signs are $-++$, implying one negative and one positive root.

3. Locate the roots of $x^3 + x^2 - 4x + 1 = 0$.

4. Locate the roots of $x^4 - 5x^2 + 8x = 10$ and evaluate a root, $1 < \alpha < 2$, to three decimal places.

5. Find the real root of $48x^3 = 3x^2 + 3x + 1$.

6. Also of $x^3 + 5x^2 + x = 27$.

7. The equation $x^3 - 3x + 1 = 0$ has three real roots, α, β, γ. Prove also that the roots of $x^3 - 3x^2 + 3 = 0$ are $\beta + \gamma + 1/\alpha$ and two similar expressions.

CHAPTER VIII

BINOMIAL AND RECIPROCAL EQUATIONS

46. The Binomial Equation. If each coefficient of

$$f(x) = a_0x^n+a_1x^{n-1}+\ldots+a^n = 0 \quad . \quad . \quad (1)$$

vanishes except two, the equation is binomial in form, and reduces, apart from zero roots, to

$$x^m-a = 0, \quad . \quad . \quad . \quad (2)$$

which is called the **binomial** equation. By means of Demoivre's theorem this can always be solved.

There are two cases, the arithmetical and the complex.

The Arithmetical Case. In this case we assume that $a>0$. The equation $x^n-a = 0$, accordingly, has not more than one positive root, by Descartes' Rule of Signs: and since $f(0)<0$, $f(\infty)>0$ it has exactly one root, which we denote by $\sqrt[n]{a}$, and call the arithmetical nth root of a. Here a may be a perfect nth power of an integer or rational fraction, in which case x is rational, or a may not be a perfect nth power of a rational number, in which case x is irrational.

Example. If $x^5-32 = 0$, $x = 2$. If $x^5-36 = 0$, x is $\sqrt[5]{36}$, an irrational number.

The root may be computed as accurately as may be desired in various ways—from a graph for preliminary location, by logarithms, by the binomial theorem, or by Horner's method.

The binomial theorem is most effective when a is nearly a perfect nth power. Here, for instance,

$$\sqrt[5]{36} = (32+4)^{1/5} = 2(1+1/8)^{1/5}$$
$$= 2(1+1/40-1/800+...)$$
$$= 2{\cdot}0475...$$

from three terms of the series. The use of a seven-figure table of logarithms hardly improves on this.

Example. Find the real root of $x^5-60 = 0$ to seven places of decimals by Horner's method, comparing the result with that given by seven-figure logarithms.

The Complex Case. Let a be written in the complex polar form

$$a = r(\cos\theta+i\sin\theta),$$

where $r>0$: and let $b^n = r$, where $b = \sqrt[n]{r}$, the arithmetical nth root of the modulus r of a. If we now put $x = by$ the equation $x^n = a$ reduces to

$$y^n = \cos\theta+i\sin\theta,$$

which is solved by taking

$$y = \cos\frac{\theta+2s\pi}{n}+i\sin\frac{\theta+2s\pi}{n},\ s = 0, 1, 2, ..., n-1.$$

Proof. If y has this value, then by Demoivre's theorem

$$y^n = \cos(\theta+2s\pi)+i\sin(\theta+2s\pi)$$
$$= \cos\theta+i\sin\theta$$

for each value of s. Hence the stated value of y is a root of the equation.

Also for the n given values of s, y takes exactly n different values, which are represented by points on a circle of unit radius whose amplitudes differ successively by $2\pi/n$; and such points lie at the n vertices of a regular polygon inscribed in the circle. Hence each possible root of this equation of the nth degree has been identified, for there cannot be more than n roots.

Furthermore, if s takes higher values n, $n+1$, ..., or else negative values, the same vertices are repeated. For

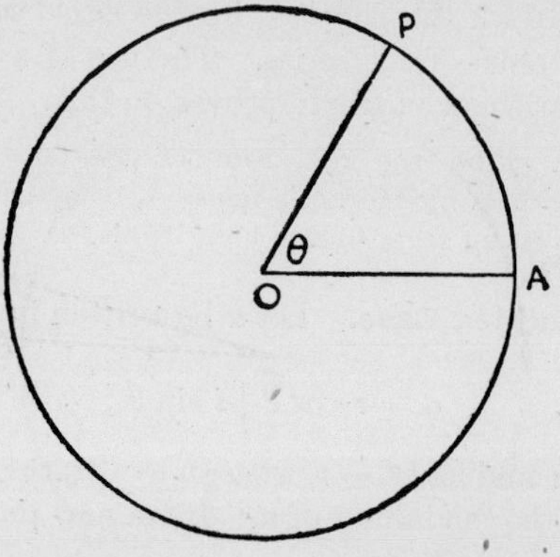

example, the point N_3 in the figure is given by $n = 6$, $s = ..., -4, 2, 8, 14, ...$.

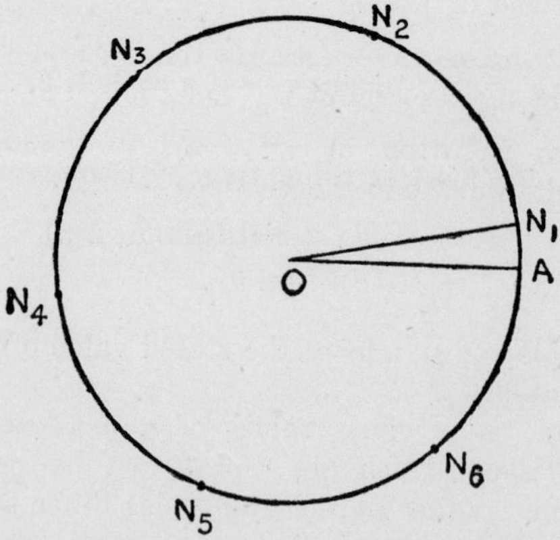

Geometrically the solutions of the equation

$$x^n = e^{i\theta} = \cos\theta + i \sin\theta$$

where θ is, of course, real, are given by the following construction: Draw a circle with centre O and of unit radius OA. Take P a point on it such that the angle AOP is θ. Mark the point N_1 on the circle such that the

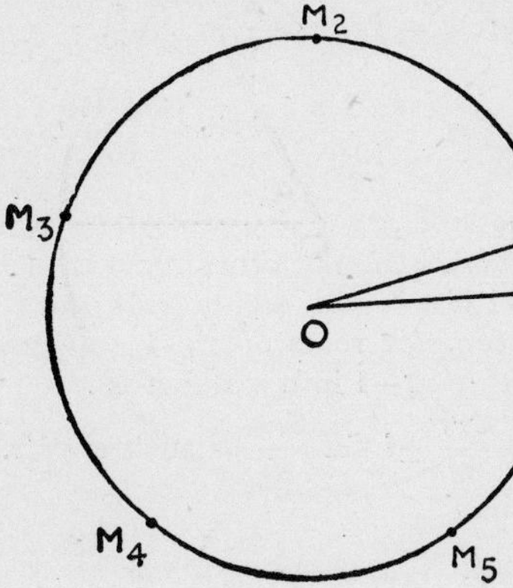

angle AON_1 is θ/n: then mark the n vertices of a regular inscribed polygon $N_1N_2...N_n$. The complex numbers answering to these n vertices are the n distinct nth roots of $e^{i\theta}$. The figures exhibit the cases $n = 5$ and 6.

General Solution of $x^n = a$. By combining the above results we obtain the n values

$$x = |a|^{1/n}\left(\cos\frac{\theta+2s\pi}{n}+i\sin\frac{\theta+2s\pi}{n}\right),\ s = 0, 1, 2, \ldots, n-1,$$

where $|a|$ denotes the modulus of a, and θ is its amplitude.

Examples.

1. $x^3+8 = 0$.

Here $a = -8 = 8(\cos\pi+i\sin\pi)$,

and so

$$x = 2\left(\cos\frac{\pi}{3}+i\sin\frac{\pi}{3}\right),\ 2(\cos\pi+i\sin\pi),\ 2\left(\cos\frac{5\pi}{3}+i\sin\frac{5\pi}{3}\right)$$

$$= 1+i\sqrt{3},\ -2,\ 1-i\sqrt{3}.$$

The regular polygon in this case is an equilateral triangle with one vertex at the point $(-2, 0)$.

2. $x^7 = 1$. Here $a = 1$, $\phi = 0$, $x = \cos\dfrac{2s\pi}{7}+i\sin\dfrac{2s\pi}{7}$.

3. $x^5 = i$. Here $a = i = \cos\dfrac{\pi}{2}+i\sin\dfrac{\pi}{2}$,

$$x = \cos\frac{(4s+1)\pi}{10}+i\sin\frac{(4s+1)\pi}{10}.$$

4. The real roots of $x^n-1 = 0$ are ± 1, if n is even, and $+1$ only, if n is odd. On the other hand, $x^n+1 = 0$ has a single real root -1 if n is odd, and no real root if n is even.

5. Group the complex roots of $x^n-1 = 0$ into conjugate pairs. Hence resolve x^n-1 into real factors.

(Take $x = \cos\dfrac{2s\pi}{n}\pm i\sin\dfrac{2s\pi}{n}$ as such a pair. Then the quadratic polynomial

$$\left(x-\cos\frac{2s\pi}{n}\right)^2+\sin^2\frac{2s\pi}{n}$$

vanishes for these two values of x; that is, $x^2-2x\cos\dfrac{2s\pi}{n}+1$ is a factor of x^n-1 for integral values of s.

If n is odd there are $\frac{1}{2}(n-1)$ such quadratic factors, where $s = 1, 2, 3, \ldots, \frac{1}{2}(n-1)$. If n is even, there are $\frac{1}{2}(n-2)$ such factors with $s = 1, 2, 3, \ldots, \frac{1}{2}(n-2)$. This accounts for all the complex factors, but there are also real linear factors, namely $(x-1)(x+1)$ when n is even, and $x-1$ when n is odd.)

6. $x^5-1 = (x-1)\left(x^2-2x\cos\dfrac{2\pi}{5}+1\right)\left(x^2-2x\cos\dfrac{4\pi}{5}+1\right)$.

7. $x^6-1 = (x^2-1)\left(x^2-2x\cos\dfrac{\pi}{3}+1\right)\left(x^2-2x\cos\dfrac{2\pi}{3}+1\right)$.

47. Euclidean Construction of the Regular Polygon. The solution of the binomial equation $x^n-1 = 0$ and the construction of a regular polygon of n vertices are evidently closely connected, and already we have considered a general trigonometrical form of the solution. But there are other more purely geometrical or algebraical methods at our disposal, and it is natural to find out how far, for instance, the time-honoured ruler and compass constructions of Euclid would carry us in forming a regular polygon of n sides. Euclid gave us the triangle, square and pentagon ($n = 3, 4, 5$) and any figure deducible from these by repeated bisection or by combination of cases. In fact whenever $n = 2^m.3.5$ a regular figure could be drawn by ruler and compass.

For example, to construct a regular 15-gon, take the arc of the pentagon, which is a fifth of the circumference, from the arc of the triangle, which is a third, and bisect the resulting arc.

But how shall we deal with such cases as $n = 7, 9$, or 11 ? Great interest has been taken in such problems throughout the ages, and notable results were found by Lagrange and Legendre, who examined the corresponding algebraic equations ; but it was Gauss who made the greatest discovery in this field since the time of Euclid, for in 1796 Gauss proved that the 17-sided regular polygon could be drawn with ruler and compass. In fact he proved that the case when

$$n = 2^{2m}+1$$

is always possible provided that n is prime. The lowest values of n satisfying this condition are $n = 3, 5, 17$, 257, 65537.

Algebraically, the use of linear and quadratic equations is equivalent to such ruler and compass constructions ; and it can be shown that the solution of the equation $x^n-1 = 0$ is reducible to that of quadratic equations by what are otherwise rational processes, in precisely those cases in which, geometrically, the ruler and compass succeed. We cannot attempt any proof here, but one illustration can be given.

Example. Take $n = 5$, $x^5-1 = 0$. Segregate the factor $x-1$, leaving

$$x^4+x^3+x^2+x+1 = 0.$$

This is a simple instance of a reciprocal equation (**48**). To solve it we put $y = x+1/x$, so that $y^2 = x^2+2+1/x^2$. Hence

$$x^2+x+1+1/x+1/x^2 = y^2+y-1 = 0.$$

We can solve this equation for y, and we can also solve the quadratic equation corresponding to the substitution,

$$x^2-xy+1 = 0,$$

as a quadratic for x in terms of y; in fact we have

$$x = \tfrac{1}{2}y \pm \sqrt{\tfrac{1}{4}y^2-1}, \text{ where } y = -\tfrac{1}{2}\pm\tfrac{1}{2}\sqrt{5}.$$

The quartic equation in x has thus been solved by the successive use of two quadratic equations.

48. Reduction of Degree of Certain Equations. Reciprocal Equations. In the first place there are certain rather special types of equation which are reducible to equations of lower degree and root extractions. It is easy, for example, to reduce equations such as

$$x^{2n}+ax^n+b = 0, \text{ or } x^{3n}+ax^{2n}+bx^n+c = 0$$

by the substitution $y = x^n$.

Examples.

$$x^6+9x^3+8 = 0, \; (x^2+3x+2)^2-4(x^2+3x+2)+3 = 0.$$

Such instances are easy to devise, but they seldom occur in practice. A more important and general case is that of the reciprocal equation:

$$a_0x^n+a_1x^{n-1}+a_2x^{n-2}+\ldots+a_2x^2+a_1x+a_0 = 0,$$

where $a_s = a_{n-s}$ for $s = 0, 1, 2, \ldots, n$.

Theorem. The reciprocal equation of even degree is rationally reducible to an equation of half that degree.

Proof. Put $z = x+1/x$, so that $z^2 = x^2+2+1/x^2$, $z^3 = x^3+3x+3/x+1/x^3$, and so on. Then

$$x+1/x = z, \; x^2+1/x^2 = z^2-2, \; x^3+1/x^3 = z^3-3z,$$

and so on. By this iteration we express

$$x^s+1/x^s \quad \text{as} \quad z^s-sz^{s-2}+\ldots,$$

that is, as a polynomial in z of degree s, for each value of s in succession. Now put $n = 2m$ and divide the given equation throughout by x^m, so that it can be rearranged as

$$a_0(x^m+1/x^m)+a_1(x^{m-1}+1/x^{m-1})+\ldots+a_m = 0.$$

Substituting for each bracketed expression its equivalent as a polynomial in z we obtain an equation in z of degree m.

Corollary. A reciprocal equation of odd degree 2m+1 *can be rationally reduced to one of degree* m.

Proof. In such a reciprocal equation $f(x) = 0$ we find at once that $f(-1)$ vanishes: hence $x+1$ is a factor of $f(x)$. If $f(x)$ is written $(x+1)\psi(x)$ then $\psi(x)$ is of degree $2m$ and is also reciprocal, since the roots of $\psi(x) = 0$ are those of $f(x) = 0$, with the root -1 removed; and the roots of $f(x) = 0$ are reciprocal (**42**, p. 98) in pairs.

The preceding theorem now applies, and reduces $f(x) = 0$ to an equation of degree m.

Analytically, $f(x) = x^n f(x^{-1})$ is the relation characteristic of a reciprocal equation $f(x) = 0$ of degree n.

Certain equations are reciprocal in respect of the numerical values of the coefficients, but alternate in the sign of the coefficients, in such wise that the terms may be grouped as

$$x-1/x,\ x^2+1/x^2,\ x^3-1/x^3,\ \ldots.$$

When this happens the transformation $z = x-1/x$ will be effective.

Other equations can sometimes be transformed to the reciprocal form. For example in

$$16x^4+8ax^3+4bx^2+2ax+1 = 0$$

we should first put $2x = y$, then $y+1/y = z$. The equation then reduces to $z^2+az+b-2 = 0$.

Examples.

1. Solve $6x^4+5x^3-38x^2+5x+6 = 0$.

(Put $x+1/x = z$. Then $6(z^2-2)+5z-38 = 0$, so that $z = 2\frac{1}{2}$ or $-3\frac{1}{3}$. Hence $x+1/x = 2\frac{1}{2}$ or $-3\frac{1}{3}$, and $x = 2, \frac{1}{2}, -3, -\frac{1}{3}$.)

2. Solve $2x^5+7x^4+9x^3+9x^2+7x+2 = 0$.

(Divide the polynomial by $x+1$, getting

$$2x^4+5x^3+4x^2+5x+2 = 0.$$

The solutions are $x = -1, -2, -\frac{1}{2}, \pm i$.)

3. Solve $2x^4+3x^3-4x^2-3x+2 = 0$.

(Put $x-1/x = z$. Solutions are $x = 1, -1, -2, \frac{1}{2}$.)

4. Solve $6x^4+35x^3+62x^2+35x+6 = 0$.

5. Prove that the points of the Gauss plane representing the five roots of $(z+1)^5 = 32z^5$ are concyclic.

6. Calculate the fourth roots of $8(-1+i\sqrt{3})$.

CHAPTER IX

THE CUBIC EQUATION

49. Historical and Introductory. Examples of cubic equations have recently been discovered by O. Neugebauer among ancient Babylonian records. Cubic equations were considered by Diophantus about A.D. 300, but the first European mathematicians to give a complete solution of them belonged to the Italian school of Bologna at the time of the Renaissance: they were Scipio Ferro, Nicolas Fontana, surnamed Tartaglia (that is, the Stammerer), and Cardan (who visited St Andrews in Scotland in 1552). The solution which usually bears the name of Cardan, who brought it into prominence, is really due to Tartaglia.

The general cubic equation is

$$x^3+a_1x^2+a_2x+a_3=0. \quad . \quad . \quad . \quad (1)$$

By taking $x=y-\frac{1}{3}a_1$ we can reduce it at once to the form

$$y^3+\left(a_2-\frac{1}{3}a_1^2\right)y+\frac{2}{27}a_1^3-\frac{1}{3}a_1a_2+a_3=0. \quad . \quad (2)$$

This equation can now be written as

$$x^3+ax+b=0 \quad . \quad . \quad . \quad (3)$$

which we shall call the *reduced* form of the cubic. It lacks a term in x^2: otherwise the coefficients are general.

If a_2 happens to be zero it is quicker to put $x=1/y$, in order to reach a reduced form of cubic equation.

50. Cardan's Solution of the Cubic. To solve

$$x^3+ax+b=0 \quad . \quad . \quad . \quad (1)$$

put $x=z+v$. Then

$$\left.\begin{aligned} x^3 &= z^3+v^3+3zv(z+v) \\ &= z^3+v^3+3zvx. \end{aligned}\right\} \quad . \quad . \quad (2)$$

Equation (2) may be regarded as a cubic equation in x and is in reduced form, since there is no term in x^2. Equations (1) and (2) are the same provided that

$$z^3+v^3=-b, \quad 3zv=-a. \quad . \quad . \quad (3)$$

To solve this pair of simultaneous eqations for z and v, write $z^3v^3=-a^3/27$, so that z^3 and v^3 are the roots of the quadratic

$$\lambda^2+b\lambda-a^3/27=0, \quad . \quad . \quad . \quad (4)$$

where the sum of the roots is $-b$, and the product of the roots, namely z^3v^3, is $-a^3/27$. Hence $\lambda=z^3$ or v^3; that is,

$$\lambda=-\tfrac{1}{2}b\pm\sqrt{(b^2/4+a^3/27)}=z^3,\ v^3. \quad . \quad (5)$$

Since z and v have entered the work symmetrically, it does not matter which is which : and so we let z^3 be given by the positive, and v^3 by the negative, sign. Finally we take the cube roots and add, so that

$$x=z+v=\sqrt[3]{\{-\tfrac{1}{2}b+\sqrt{(b^2/4+a^3/27)}\}}+\sqrt[3]{\{-\tfrac{1}{2}b-\sqrt{(b^2/4+a^3/27)}\}} \ . \ (6)$$

This is the celebrated formula of Cardan (1573).

Example. $\quad x^3+3x+8=0.$

Here $x=z+v$, $z^3+v^3=-8$, $zv=-1$ and $\lambda^2+8\lambda-1=0$, so that $\lambda=-4\pm\sqrt{17}$.

Thus $\quad x=\sqrt[3]{(-4+\sqrt{17})}+\sqrt[3]{(-4-\sqrt{17})}$.

Since every number has three distinct cube roots (p. 109) we have evidently obtained several values of x by Cardan's formula. This is as it should be, for a cubic equation usually has three distinct roots. But at first sight it appears that there are nine, or even eighteen, possibilities in the formula, since alternative solutions exist for square and also for cube roots. As for square roots, a glance shows that the signs are fixed—one must be positive and one negative. Accordingly we consider the cube roots.

Let the distinct roots of $x^3-1=0$ be $1, \omega, \omega^2$, so that

$$1+\omega+\omega^2=0, \quad \omega=-\tfrac{1}{2}+i\frac{\sqrt{3}}{2}, \quad \omega^2=-\tfrac{1}{2}-i\frac{\sqrt{3}}{2}.$$

Then $\omega^3=1$, and the cubes of $z, \omega z, \omega^2 z$ are each equal to z^3. Similarly for v. Hence there are three-times-three ways of taking the formula (6) for x, owing to these combinations of the pair of cube roots. But whereas each of the nine ways will satisfy the first condition

$$z^3+v^3=-b \quad (e.g.\ (\omega z)^3+(\omega v)^3=-b)$$

only three ways will satisfy $3zv=-a$, namely z with v, ωz with $\omega^2 v$, and $\omega^2 z$ with ωv. We infer that the three roots for x are given by the formulae

$$x=z+v,\ \omega z+\omega^2 v,\ \omega^2 z+\omega v, \quad . \quad . \quad (7)$$

where z and v are the cube root expressions of (6).

A check upon the accuracy of this result is afforded by adding together these three roots. The sum is

$$(1+\omega+\omega^2)(z+v),$$

which vanishes since $1+\omega+\omega^2=0$.

Example. $\qquad x^3-18x-35=0.$

Here $\qquad x=2+3,\ 2\omega+3\omega^2,\ 2\omega^2+3\omega,$

$$=5,\ -\frac{5}{2}\mp i\frac{\sqrt{3}}{2}.$$

The sum of the roots is zero.

51. The Case of Equal Roots. If two of the roots are equal we equate a pair of the results **50** (7). For example, let $z+v=\omega z+\omega^2 v$, so that $(1-\omega)z=(\omega^2-1)v$

and $z = (-1-\omega)v = \omega^2 v$. From the three possible pairings of roots we find that when

$$z = v \text{ or } \omega v \text{ or } \omega^2 v \quad . \quad . \quad . \quad (1)$$

two roots are equal. Substituting in **50** (3) we have

$$2v^3 = -b, \quad -a = 3v^2 \text{ or } 3\omega v^2 \text{ or } 3\omega^2 v^2,$$

so that $4v^6 = b^2$, $27v^6 = -a^3$ in each case. Hence

$$\Delta = b^2/4 + a^3/27 = 0. \quad . \quad . \quad . \quad (2)$$

The expression on the left side of this equation is called the *discriminant*. Conversely, if this discriminant vanishes then $z = v$ or ωv or $\omega^2 v$, as we see from **50** (4), for both z and v are in this case cube roots of $-\frac{1}{2}b$: and accordingly two roots are equal.

Three roots of the equation $x^3+ax+b = 0$ are equal when and only when $a = b = 0$, as is seen by making all the values (1) equal, so that $z = v = 0$. In this case the unreduced equation is more interesting, and the condition for three equal roots is that

$$x^3+a_1x^2+a_2x+a_3$$

should be a perfect cube. If so, it must take the form $(x-\alpha)^3$, and therefore $a_1 = -3\alpha$, $a_2 = +3\alpha^2$, $a_3 = -\alpha^3$. This requires two conditions to connect the three coefficients : for example,

$$a_1^2+3a_2 = 0, \quad a_1a_2-9a_3 = 0.$$

The expression Δ is not only the discriminant of the cubic but also of equation **50** (4), which is called the *quadratic resolvent*. We shall now see that it discriminates further between real and complex roots.

52. The Ordinary Case $\Delta>0$. If the quantity

$$\Delta = b^2/4+a^3/27$$

is positive the formula **50** (4) gives real values of both z and v, so that $x = z+v$ is also real. In this case the other two values of x are $\omega z+\omega^2 v$ and $\omega^2 z+\omega v$. But

$$\omega = -\tfrac{1}{2}+i\,\tfrac{1}{2}\sqrt{3}\,;$$

hence these values of x are

$$-\tfrac{1}{2}(z+v)\pm\tfrac{1}{2}i\sqrt{3}(z-v),$$

which are necessarily complex, since $z-v$ cannot vanish unless $\Delta = 0$, whereas Δ has just been assumed to be positive. We infer that *when $\Delta>0$ two roots are necessarily complex, and one only is real.*

The Irreducible Case, $\Delta<0$. The above certainly suggests that the outstanding possibility, namely the case when $\Delta<0$, furnishes the criterion for the existence of three real roots x, which is indeed the case. In fact, if $\Delta<0$, then the quadratic of **50** (4) for λ has complex conjugate roots, giving, let us say,

$$z^3 = p+iq, \quad v^3 = p-iq, \qquad . \qquad . \qquad (3)$$

where $p = -\tfrac{1}{2}b$ and $q = \sqrt{(-\Delta)}$, which are both real. It is possible to proceed by using Demoivre's theorem, after putting

$$p = r\cos\theta, \quad q = r\sin\theta,$$

so that r and θ are real. Then, by Cardan's formula,

$$x = \sqrt[3]{(p+iq)}+\sqrt[3]{(p-iq)}$$

$$= r^{\frac{1}{3}}(\cos\theta+i\sin\theta)^{\frac{1}{3}}+r^{\frac{1}{3}}(\cos\theta-i\sin\theta)^{\frac{1}{3}}$$

$$= r^{\frac{1}{3}}\left(\cos\frac{\theta+2k\pi}{3}+i\sin\frac{\theta+2k\pi}{3}+\cos\frac{\theta+2k\pi}{3}-i\sin\frac{\theta+2k\pi}{3}\right)$$

$$= 2r^{\frac{1}{3}}\cos\frac{\theta+2k\pi}{3}, \text{ where } k \text{ is any integer} \quad . \quad . \quad . \quad (4)$$

Incidentally we have satisfied the condition $3zv = -a$, where a is of course real, by taking the same value of k in extracting the cube roots of $p+iq$ and $p-iq$. In other words, z and v are conjugate complex numbers.

By taking $k = 0, 1, 2$ we obtain three distinct values of $\cos\dfrac{\theta+2k\pi}{3}$ and therefore of x, each of which satisfies the cubic equation, so that we have discovered the requisite roots. Taking further integer values of k merely repeats the same values of x, owing to the identity $\cos\left(\dfrac{\theta}{3}+2\pi\right) = \cos\dfrac{\theta}{3}$. Furthermore, these roots are all real. Hence if $\Delta<0$ all three roots are real.

Conversely, if all three roots are real, then $z+v$ must be real, so that z and v must be conjugate complex numbers $h\pm ik$; and it is easy to verify that each of the three roots as given by $z+v$, $\omega z+\omega^2 v$, $\omega^2 v+\omega v$ is real. Hence

$$\begin{aligned}\Delta &= b^2/4+a^3/27 = \tfrac{1}{4}(z^3+v^3)^2-z^3v^3\\ &= \tfrac{1}{4}(z^3-v^3)^2 = (3ihk^2+i^3k^3)^2 = -(3h-k)^2k^4.\end{aligned}$$

This expression is either zero (giving the case already treated in **51** of two equal roots) or is negative. Hence *if the roots are real and unequal then* $\Delta<0$.

Once more, in this case, $p = -\tfrac{1}{2}b$, $q = \sqrt{(-\Delta)}$, so that

$$r^2 = p^2+q^2 = \tfrac{1}{4}b^2-\Delta = -(a/3)^3,$$

while $r\cos\theta = p$, that is,

$$\cos\theta = -b/2\sqrt{(-a^3/27)}. \qquad . \quad . \quad (5)$$

Hence

$$x = 2\sqrt[6]{\frac{-a^3}{27}}\cos\frac{\theta+2k\pi}{3}, \quad k = 0, 1, 2. \quad . \quad (6)$$

We call this the *trigonometrical solution* of the cubic equation.

To sum up: if a and b are real the cubic equation $x^3+ax+b = 0$ has

(i) three real roots when $\Delta<0$,
(ii) two equal roots if $\Delta = 0$,
(iii) one real and two complex roots if $\Delta>0$.

Here $\Delta = b^2/4+a^3/27$: it is the discriminant both of the cubic and of the resolvent quadratic $\lambda^2+b\lambda-a^3/27 = 0$.

In case (i) z and v are conjugate complex numbers, in case (ii) they are real and equal, in case (iii) they are real and unequal.

Cardan's formula at once yields the *real* roots in cases (ii) and (iii), but, paradoxically, cannot do so in case (i) without introducing imaginary numbers. To mathematicians of the sixteenth and seventeenth centuries this feature was very mysterious: they spoke of the *irreducible* case. The method of Demoivre clears the matter up and yields the roots; but it still remains a curious fact that from a real cubic three real roots cannot be extracted by Cardan's algebraic formula without a circuitous passage into, and out of, the domain of complex numbers. (See **53**.)

Examples.

1. $x^3+12x-112 = 0$. (*Cf.* p. 148, Ex. **11.**)

Cardan's formula gives

$$\begin{aligned} x &= \sqrt[3]{\{56+\sqrt{(3136+64)}\}}+\sqrt[3]{\{56-\sqrt{(3136+64)}\}} \\ &= \sqrt[3]{112\cdot 56854}+\sqrt[3]{(-0\cdot 56854)} \\ &= 4\cdot 828\ldots-0\cdot 828\ldots = 4. \end{aligned}$$

The answer is exactly 4, but the working involves the use of tables. For the other roots, divide by $x-4$. Then

$$x^2+4x+28 = 0, \text{ and } x = -2\pm i2\sqrt{6}.$$

2. Solve $x^3+3x^2+15x+25 = 0$.

Put $x+1 = y$, then $y^3+12y+12 = 0$.

Here $a = 12$, $b = 12$, $\Delta = 100$ and

$$y = \sqrt[3]{(-6+10)}+\sqrt[3]{(-6-10)} = 1\cdot 5874-2\cdot 5198 = -0\cdot 9324,$$

so that $x = y-1 = -1\cdot 9324$. This is the only real root. Complex roots for y are given by

$$\omega\sqrt[3]{4}-\omega^2 2\sqrt[3]{2} \text{ and } \omega^2\sqrt[3]{4}-\omega 2\sqrt[3]{2}.$$

To evaluate them, call them $\alpha+i\beta$, $\alpha-i\beta$; then

$$-2\alpha = -0{\cdot}9324,$$

since the sum of the three roots must be zero. Also the product of the roots is -12. Thus $2\alpha(\alpha^2+\beta^2) = 12$, or $\beta^2 = 6/\alpha-\alpha^2$. Finally $\alpha = 0{\cdot}4662$, $\beta = 3{\cdot}5571$ and

$$x = y-1 = \alpha-1\pm i\beta = -0{\cdot}5338\pm 3{\cdot}5571i.$$

53. Alternative Trigonometrical Treatment. If real roots only are required we may proceed as follows. Consider the identity

$$4\cos^3\phi-3\cos\phi = \cos 3\phi \quad . \quad . \quad (1)$$

and suppose $x^3+ax+b = 0$. If these two equations are the same, then, on comparing coefficients, we have

$$x^3/(4\cos^3\phi) = -ax/(3\cos\phi) = -b/\cos 3\phi$$

so that $\quad -3x^2 = 4a\cos^2\phi$, or $x = 2\surd(-\tfrac{1}{3}a)\cos\phi$

and $\quad b = 2\surd(-a^3/27)\cos 3\phi.$

Thus $\cos 3\phi$ is known in terms of a and b, whence x is known. It leads to the result **52** (6) on writing $\tfrac{1}{3}a\cos\tfrac{1}{3}(\theta+2k\pi)$ for $\cos\phi$, and thus it solves the case of three real roots.

Now $\cos 3\phi$ cannot exceed unity : hence

$$b\leqslant -2\surd(-a^3/27),$$

so that $\quad \Delta = b^2/4+a^3/27\leqslant 0.$

(i) If, here, $\Delta = 0$, then $\cos 3\phi = \pm 1$, or $\phi = 2k\pi/3$ and $\cos\phi = 1, -\tfrac{1}{2}, -\tfrac{1}{2}$ according as $k = 0, 1, 2$. This gives

$$x = 2\alpha, -\alpha, -\alpha$$

as roots, where $\alpha = \surd(-a/3)$. It is the case of repeated roots, as we have seen already in **51**.

(ii) If $\Delta<0$, then

$$x = 2\surd(-a/3)\cos\left(\phi+\frac{2k\pi}{3}\right),\ k = 0, 1, 2.$$

When, however, $\Delta > 0$, $\cos 3\phi$ is greater than unity. We obtain a real result by assuming

$$x = 2\sqrt{(-a/3)}\cosh\phi,\ b = 2\sqrt{(-a^3/27)}\cosh 3\phi,\ \Delta > 0,$$

since $4\cosh^3\phi - 3\cosh\phi = \cosh 3\phi$. Since $\cosh 3\phi$ is non-periodic as a real function, it is impossible to obtain further real roots. Indeed, as we already know from **52**, the other two roots are complex.

Examples.

1. $x^3 - 3x + 1 = 0$.

Here $a = -3$, $b = 1$, $\Delta = -\frac{3}{4} < 0$.

Take $r^2 = -a^3/27 = 1$, $\cos\theta = -b/2r = -\frac{1}{2}$, so that $\theta = 120°$. Then

$$x = 2\cos\left(\frac{120+360k}{3}\right)^\circ = 2\cos 40°,\ 2\cos 160°,\ 2\cos 280°.$$

2. Solve $x^3 - 27x + 27 = 0$.

3. Solve $x^3 - 6x - 9 = 0$.

54. The Equation of Squared Differences of the Roots. Let α, β, γ be the roots of the cubic equation $x^3 + ax + b = 0$, and let us seek an equation whose roots are $(\beta-\gamma)^2$, $(\gamma-\alpha)^2$, $(\alpha-\beta)^2$.

We take $y = (\beta-\gamma)^2 = \alpha^2+\beta^2+\gamma^2 - 2\alpha\beta\gamma/\alpha - \alpha^2$.

But, by **28** (3), $\alpha+\beta+\gamma = 0$, $\beta\gamma+\gamma\alpha+\alpha\beta = a$, $\alpha\beta\gamma = -b$, so that $\alpha^2+\beta^2+\gamma^2 = (\alpha+\beta+\gamma)^2 - 2(\beta\gamma+\gamma\alpha+\alpha\beta) = -2a$.

Therefore $y = -2a + 2b/\alpha - \alpha^2 = (2b - 2a\alpha - \alpha^3)/\alpha$.

But $\alpha^3 + a\alpha + b = 0$.

Hence $(y+a)\alpha = 3b$ or $\alpha = 3b/(y+a)$.

On substituting this value of α in the cubic we have

$$y^3 + 6ay^2 + 9a^2y + 4a^3 + 27b^2 = 0 \quad . \quad . \quad (1)$$

Now one root of this new cubic is $y = (\beta-\gamma)^2$. Hence, by symmetry, the other roots are $(\gamma-\alpha)^2$, $(\alpha-\beta)^2$. Also, the product of these three roots is $-(4a^3+27b^2)$, which is $-108\,\Delta$.

Thus $$(\beta-\gamma)^2(\gamma-\alpha)^2(\alpha-\beta)^2 = -108\,\Delta \quad . \quad (2)$$

This is an important result, for it expresses the discriminant Δ explicitly as a symmetric function of the roots. It verifies (i) that Δ vanishes when, and only when, two roots are equal, (ii) that $\Delta<0$ when all the roots are real and unequal, and (iii) that $\Delta>0$ when two of the roots are complex conjugate.

55. The General Cubic Equation. Let us now consider the general cubic equation

$$a_0x^3+3a_1x^2+3a_2x+a_3 = 0, \quad . \quad . \quad (1)$$

where for convenience in what follows the binomial coefficients 1, 3, 3, 1 are inserted. If $z = a_0x+a_1$, then

$$z^3+3(a_0a_2-a_1^2)z+a_0^2a_3-3a_0a_1a_2+2a_1^3 = 0 \quad . \quad (2)$$

as is easy to verify. It is usual to write

$$H = a_0a_2-a_1^2, \quad G = a_0^2a_3-3a_0a_1a_2+2a_1^3 \quad . \quad (3)$$

If α, β, γ are the roots of the cubic in x, then the roots for z are evidently

$$a_0\alpha+a_1, \quad a_0\beta+a_1, \quad a_0\gamma+a_1 . \quad . \quad . \quad (4)$$

But $a_0\alpha+a_1-(a_0\beta+a_1) = a_0(\alpha-\beta)$, which is the difference of the roots for z. Also the preceding result **54** (2) applies to the equation for z, since this lacks a term in z^2; and we shall have

$$a_0^2(\beta-\gamma)^2a_0^2(\gamma-\alpha)^2a_0^2(\alpha-\beta)^2 = -108\,\Delta, \quad . \quad (5)$$

where

$$\Delta = b^2/4+a^3/27 = G^2/4+27H^3/27 = \tfrac{1}{4}(G^2+4H^3) \quad . \quad (6)$$

Hence, in terms of the roots α, β, γ of the general equation

$$a_0x^3+3a_1x^2+3a_2x+a_3 = 0,$$

we have

$$a_0^6(\beta-\gamma)^2(\gamma-\alpha)^2(\alpha-\beta)^2 = -27(G^2+4H^3) = -108\,\Delta . \quad (7)$$

This exhibits the discriminant Δ in a more general light: it is called the discriminant also of the more general cubic, and the characteristic properties remain true of this cubic according as $\Delta > = < 0$.

Since $3H$ and G have taken the place of a and b in the original treatment, we can sum up as follows:

The general cubic has three unequal roots if $G^2+4H^3<0$, has one real and two complex roots if $G^2+4H^3>0$, and two equal roots if $G^2+4H^3=0$.

It has three equal roots if $G=H=0$, for in this case we find at once that $a_0/a_1=a_1/a_2=a_2/a_3$, and the cubic in x becomes $(a_0x+a_1)^3=0$.

56. The Canonical Form of a Cubic. The coefficients a_i of a cubic

$$a_0x^3+3a_1x^2+3a_2x+a_3 \quad . \quad . \quad (1)$$

may be regarded as the first four coefficients of a recurring series

$$S=a_0+a_1t+a_2t^2+\ldots+a_nt^n+\ldots, \quad . \quad (2)$$

where

$$a_n=ua_{n-1}+va_{n-2} \quad . \quad . \quad . \quad (3)$$

is the scale of relation (23), p. 53, and

$$a_0v+a_1u-a_2=0,\ a_1v+a_2u-a_3=0 \quad . \quad . \quad (4)$$

are the initial equations which give u and v. Thus

$$\frac{u}{a_0a_3-a_1a_2}=\frac{-v}{a_1a_3-a_2^2}=\frac{1}{a_0a_2-a_1^2} \quad . \quad . \quad (5)$$

By the usual procedure (p. 54) the sum S is given as

$$S=\{a_0+(a_1-ua_0)t\}/(1-ut-vt^2) \quad . \quad . \quad (6)$$

which breaks up into partial fractions

$$\frac{p}{1+\alpha t}+\frac{q}{1+\beta t} \quad . \quad . \quad . \quad (7)$$

when $\alpha \neq \beta$, that is, when $u^2+4v \neq 0$. Here α, β are given by the identity

$$(1-ut-vt^2) = (1+\alpha t)(1+\beta t), \quad . \quad . \quad (8)$$

so that α and β are the roots of the quadratic

$$x^2+ux-v = 0,$$

or $$(a_0a_2-a_1^2)x^2+(a_0a_3-a_1a_2)x+(a_1a_3-a_2^2) = 0, \quad . \quad (9)$$

which is called (Aitken, *Determinants and Matrices*, p. 130) the *Hessian* of the original cubic (1). The reader may verify that the Hessian has equal roots when Δ vanishes. The Hessian can be written also in the alternative forms

$$\begin{vmatrix} a_0x+a_1 & a_1x+a_2 \\ a_1x+a_2 & a_2x+a_3 \end{vmatrix} = 0, \quad \begin{vmatrix} a_0 & a_1 & a_2 \\ a_1 & a_2 & a_3 \\ 1 & -x & x^2 \end{vmatrix} = 0. \quad . \quad (10)$$

On expanding the series for (7) and comparing the result with the series S, we have

$$p+q = a_0,\ p\alpha+q\beta = -a_1,\ p\alpha^2+q\beta^2 = a_2,\ p\alpha^3+q\beta^3 = -a_3 \quad . \quad (11)$$

Multiply these by x^3, $-3x^2$, $3x$, -1 respectively and add; then

$$p(x-\alpha)^3+q(x-\beta)^3 \equiv a_0x^3+3a_1x^2+3a_2x+a_3. \quad . \quad (12)$$

Since p and q are known by the method of partial fractions, *we have thus expressed a cubic as the sum of two cubes of linear forms.*

This is called the *canonical form* of the cubic, and the reduction to such a form is possible, whenever the roots of the Hessian are distinct, that is, when $\Delta \neq 0$.

The result is due to Sylvester, who showed that the same method would apply to any form of an odd order, cubic, quintic, septimic and so on. For a quintic

$$Q = a_0x^5+5a_1x^4+10a_2x^3+10a_3x^2+5a_4x+a_5 \quad . \quad (13)$$

we take a recurring series $S = \Sigma a_n t^n$ as before, but with a scale of relation

$$a_3 = a_2u+a_1v+a_0w,\ a_4 = a_3u+a_2v+a_1w, \text{ etc.}, \quad . \quad (14)$$

where $$(1-ut-vt^2-wt^3) = (1+\alpha t)(1+\beta t)(1+\gamma t) \quad . \quad (15)$$

and $$S = \frac{p}{1+\alpha t}+\frac{q}{1+\beta t}+\frac{r}{1+\gamma t} = \sum_{n=0}^{\infty} a_n t^n. \qquad (16)$$

The quintic is readily found to be

$$Q = p(x-\alpha)^5+q(x-\beta)^5+r(x-\gamma)^5,$$

where α, β, γ are the roots of the cubic

$$x^3+ux^2-vx+w = 0,$$

or

$$\begin{vmatrix} a_0x+a_1 & a_1x+a_2 & a_2x+a_3 \\ a_1x+a_2 & a_2x+a_3 & a_3x+a_4 \\ a_2x+a_3 & a_3x+a_4 & a_4x+a_5 \end{vmatrix} = 0, \text{ or } \begin{vmatrix} a_0 & a_1 & a_2 & a_3 \\ a_1 & a_2 & a_3 & a_4 \\ a_2 & a_3 & a_4 & a_5 \\ 1 & -x & x^2 & -x^3 \end{vmatrix} = 0. \qquad (17)$$

The determinant, of order n when the original form is of order $2n-1$, is called the *canonizant* of the form. The method also applies when the roots of the canonizant are repeated: we then modify the partial fractions in the usual way and proceed as before.

Examples.

1. If, for the cubic, $\alpha = \beta$,

then $$S = \frac{p}{1+\alpha t}+\frac{q}{(1+\alpha t)^2}$$

and the canonical form is

$$r(x-\alpha)^3+s(x-\alpha)^2, \text{ where } r = p+q,\ s = -3q\alpha.$$

2. Reduce x^3-3x+2 to canonical form

$$(\alpha = \beta = 1;\ (x-1)^3+3(x-1)^2).$$

3. Reduce $9x^3-6x^2+18x+7$.

4. If α, β, γ are the roots of a cubic and ω is a complex cube root of unity, prove that the roots of the Hessian are

$$\frac{\beta\gamma+\omega\gamma\alpha+\omega^2\alpha\beta}{\alpha+\omega\beta+\omega^2\gamma},\quad \frac{\beta\gamma+\omega^2\gamma\alpha+\omega\alpha\beta}{\alpha+\omega^2\beta+\omega\gamma}.$$

CHAPTER X

THE BIQUADRATIC OR QUARTIC EQUATION

57. The Quartic Equation: Feasibility of a Solution by Radicals. The equation

$$f \equiv f(x) = a_0x^4+4a_1x^3+6a_2x^2+4a_3x+a_4 = 0 \quad . \quad (1)$$

is called a *biquadratic* or *quartic* equation. In general it has four roots α, β, γ, δ which can be found algebraically by reducing the equation to a cubic equation in rational steps. Since it is known that equations of degree higher than the fourth cannot be so reduced to lower equations it is of interest to enquire why a quartic admits such a reduction. The underlying reason is simply this: that if a cubic equation

$$z^3+pz^2+qz+r = 0 \quad . \quad . \quad . \quad (2)$$

is formed, the roots of which are

$$\beta\gamma+\alpha\delta,\ \gamma\alpha+\beta\delta,\ \alpha\beta+\gamma\delta, \quad . \quad . \quad . \quad (3)$$

then each of its coefficients is a symmetric function of α, β, γ, δ. (This is easily verified: for instance the sum of the three roots is $\Sigma\beta\gamma$.) Accordingly, p, q, r are known rational functions of the original a_0, a_1, a_2, a_3, a_4. But the cubic can be solved; so that $\beta\gamma+\alpha\delta$ is known. Also $\alpha\beta\gamma\delta = a_4/a_0$. Thus we can obtain $\beta\gamma$ and $\alpha\delta$ as roots of a quadratic. Similarly for all six binary products $\beta\gamma$. Hence each ratio $\alpha\beta : \alpha\gamma$ and therefore $\beta : \gamma$ is known, from which we can find not merely the ratios of the roots but the roots themselves by using the fact that $\Sigma\alpha = -4a_1/a_0$.

58. Ferrari's Method of Solution. Let the quartic f

of **57** (1) be multiplied by a_0 and then expressed as the difference of two squares

$$(a_0x^2+2a_1x+a_2+2a_0\theta)^2-(2Mx+N)^2, \quad . \quad . \quad (1)$$

where, it will be seen, the coefficients of x^4 and x^3 agree with those of the original, multiplied by a_0. Comparison of the further terms in x^2, x^1 and x^0 gives us the relations :

$$M^2 = a_1^2-a_0a_2+a_0^2\theta,\quad MN = a_1a_2-a_0a_3+2a_0a_1\theta,$$
$$N^2 = (a_2+2a_0\theta)^2-a_0a_4. \quad . \quad . \quad (2)$$

Eliminating M and N by squaring MN and equating the result to M^2N^2, we find that

$$4a_0^3\theta^3-a_0I\theta+J = 0, \quad . \quad . \quad . \quad (3)$$

where

$$I = a_0a_4-4a_1a_3+3a_2^2, \qquad J = \begin{vmatrix} a_0 & a_1 & a_2 \\ a_1 & a_2 & a_3 \\ a_2 & a_3 & a_4 \end{vmatrix} \quad . \quad . \quad (4)$$

The equation (3), which is usually called Euler's *reducing cubic*, is typical of the reduction ; for whatever algebraic method of solution for the quartic is attempted, sooner or later such a *cubic resolvent* is bound to arise.

Let u, v, w be the roots of the cubic. From one such root u we at once find the values of M^2 and MN uniquely. Hence M and N are known, apart from a sign which is immaterial, since the result gives us simultaneously the quadratic factors

$$a_0x^2+2a_1x+a_2+2a_0\theta\pm(2Mx+N) \quad . \quad . \quad (5)$$

of the quartic a_0f. On solving these quadratics we obtain the four roots α, β, γ, δ of the original quartic.

Examples. (See also Example 5, p. 139.)

1. Solve $x^4+6x^2+8x+21 = 0$.

Here $a_0 = 1$, $a_1 = 0$, $a_2 = 1$, $a_3 = 2$, $a_4 = 21$, $I = 24$, $J = 16$ and $\theta^3-6\theta+4 = 0$, which is solved by $\theta = 2$. The equation now becomes

$$(x^2+1+4)^2-(2Mx+N)^2 = 0,$$

giving $M = \pm 1$ and $N = \mp 2$. Thus we have x^2+2x+3 and x^2-2x+7 as factors.

The roots are $-1 \pm i\sqrt{2}$, $1 \pm i\sqrt{6}$.

2. Solve the equations

(i) $x^4-4x^2+9x+4 = 0$, $(2M = -2N = 3)$

(ii) $x^4+6x^3+14x^2+15x+4 = 0$.

Obviously the quadratic equations obtained by factorizing the quartic in the form (1) above can themselves be factorized in terms of the roots of the quartic, so that we shall have

$$a_0x^2+2a_1x+a_2+2a_0u+2Mx+N = a_0(x-\alpha)(x-\beta), \quad (6)$$
$$a_0x^2+2a_1x+a_2+2a_0u-2Mx-N = a_0(x-\gamma)(x-\delta),$$

in order that the product of the two quadratics may be $a_0^2\Pi(x-\alpha)$ or a_0f. Since the four factors $x-\alpha$ may be paired in three ways, as $(\alpha\beta, \gamma\delta)$, $(\alpha\gamma, \beta\delta)$, $(\alpha\delta, \beta\gamma)$, we have another explanation of the existence of a cubic equation for θ. The triple pairings will correspond to the three possible values u, v, w of θ when substituted in (6).

By comparing coefficients of powers of x in (6) we have

$$2a_1+2M = -a_0(\alpha+\beta), \quad a_2+2a_0u+N = a_0\alpha\beta,$$
$$2a_1-2M = -a_0(\gamma+\delta), \quad a_2+2a_0u-N = a_0\gamma\delta,$$

so that $\quad a_0(\alpha\beta+\gamma\delta) = 2a_2+4a_0u,$

Similarly, $\quad a_0(\alpha\gamma+\beta\delta) = 2a_2+4a_0v,$

$$a_0(\alpha\delta+\beta\gamma) = 2a_2+4a_0w. \quad (7)$$

Since θ^2 is absent in the cubic $u+v+w$ must vanish.

Hence $2(\alpha\beta+\gamma\delta)-(\alpha\gamma+\beta\delta)-(\alpha\delta+\beta\gamma) = 8u-4v-4w = 12u$,

or $$12u = (\alpha-\delta)(\beta-\gamma)+(\alpha-\gamma)(\beta-\delta). \quad (8)$$

This gives a root u of the cubic explicitly in terms of those of the quartic. Analogous formulae hold for v and w, namely,

$$12v = (\alpha-\beta)(\gamma-\delta)+(\alpha-\delta)(\gamma-\beta),$$
$$12w = (\alpha-\beta)(\delta-\gamma)+(\alpha-\gamma)(\delta-\beta).$$

By subtraction we find that

$$4(u-v) = (\alpha-\delta)(\beta-\gamma) \quad . \quad . \quad . \quad (9)$$

and two similar expressions for $v-w$, $w-u$. Hence, by multiplying all three results of this type together, we have

$$64(v-w)(w-u)(u-v) = (\alpha-\delta)(\beta-\gamma)(\alpha-\beta)(\gamma-\delta)(\alpha-\gamma)(\delta-\beta) \quad (10)$$

When $u = 0$ the four numbers α, β, γ, δ are said to be *harmonically separated*, and the relation is often written as

$$\{\alpha\beta, \gamma\delta\} \equiv \frac{(\alpha-\gamma)(\beta-\delta)}{(\alpha-\delta)(\beta-\gamma)} = -1. \quad . \quad . \quad . \quad (11)$$

In this case one root of the cubic vanishes : hence $J = 0$. Conversely, if $J = 0$ the four roots of the quartic form harmonic pairs.

If $\alpha = \beta$, then $v = w$, as is seen at once from (7). *Hence both quartic and cubic have repeated roots.* By **51**, p. 120, the condition for this is that

$$\Delta = I^3-27J^2 = 0. \quad . \quad . \quad . \quad (12)$$

This expression Δ is called the *discriminant* of the quartic. It will now be proved that

$$a_0^6(\beta-\gamma)^2(\gamma-\alpha)^2(\alpha-\beta)^2(\alpha-\delta)^2(\beta-\delta)^2(\gamma-\delta)^2 = 256\,\Delta, \quad (13)$$

For by **54**, p. 126, we have

$$\begin{aligned} \Pi(u-v)^2 &= 108(I^3/27-J^2)/64a_0^6 \\ &= (I^3-27J^2)/16a_0^6 \\ &= \Delta/16a_0^6. \end{aligned}$$

Hence, by (10),

$$a_0^6\Pi(\alpha-\beta)^2 = a_0^6\ 64^2\Pi(u-v)^2 = 256\,\Delta.$$

Example. For $x^4-1 = 0$ we find $I = -1$, $J = 0$, $4\theta^3+\theta = 0$, and the roots of the quartic are ± 1, $\pm i$, while those of the reducing cubic are 0, $\pm\frac{1}{2}i$.

The reader can prove from (13) that $\Delta<0$ is the condition for two real and two complex roots, $\Delta>0$ is that for four real or four complex roots. (*Cf.* Burnside and Panton, *Theory of Equations* (1899), vol. 1, p. 145.)

59. Geometrical Aspect of the Quartic Equation. Let us consider the locus $x = t^2$, $y = 2t$. It is the parametric form of a parabola S whose equation is $y^2 = 4x$. If

$$S' = ax^2+2hxy+by^2+2gx+2fy+c = 0 \quad . \quad (1)$$

denotes another conic, then the points common to the two curves S and S' are given by

$$at^4+2ht^3+4bt^2+2gt^2+4ft+c = 0, \quad . \quad . \quad (2)$$

which is a quartic equation for t. It has in general four solutions α, β, γ, δ, giving four points $A = (\alpha^2, 2\alpha)$, and so on, all of which lie on each conic S and S'.

Now consider the conic

$$F = a_0x^2+2a_1xy+a_2y^2+2a_2x+2a_3y+a_4 = 0. \quad . \quad (3)$$

It meets the parabola where

$$a_0t^4+4a_1t^3+6a_2t^2+4a_3t+a_4 = 0. \quad . \quad . \quad (4)$$

Also the points A, B, C, D common to F and S lie on the conic

$$G \equiv F-a_0\theta(y^2-4x) = 0 \quad . \quad . \quad (5)$$

for all values of θ. The discriminant of this conic vanishes if

$$\begin{vmatrix} a_0 & a_1 & a_2+2a_0\theta \\ a_1 & a_2-a_0\theta & a_3 \\ a_2+2a_0\theta & a_3 & a_4 \end{vmatrix} = 0, \quad . \quad . \quad (6)$$

as is at once apparent by writing out F in full and rearranging the terms. On expansion this condition turns out to be the reducing cubic

$$4a_0{}^3\theta^3-a_0I\theta+J = 0. \quad . \quad . \quad . \quad (7)$$

The three roots of this equation give three values of θ for which the conic G degenerates into two straight lines; and, since the lines must pass through the four points A, B, C, D, they can only be the pairs AB, CD; AC, BD;

AD, BC. In either case G resolves into factors linear in x and y, or quadratic factors in t. But when $x = t^2$ and $y = 2t$ are substituted in the expression G the terms involving θ disappear, so that G takes the same form as

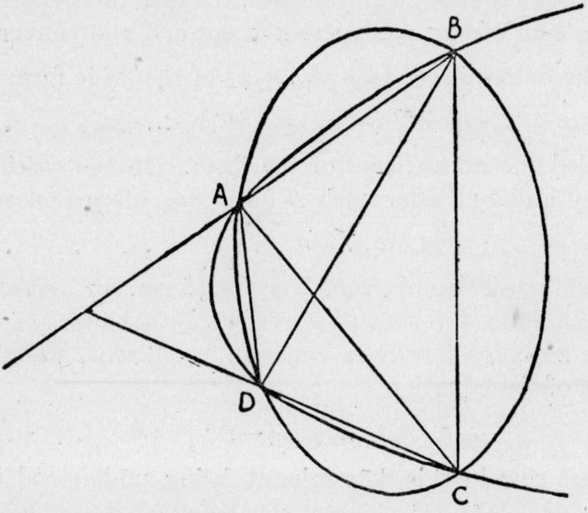

F; that is, G becomes the quartic in t. Hence we have factorized this quartic into two quadratic factors by choosing θ to satisfy the reducing cubic.

60. Canonical Forms of Even Order. Suppose we have

$$a_0v+a_1u-a_2 = 0,\ a_1v+a_2u-a_3 = 0,\ a_2v+a_3u-a_4 = 0. \quad (1)$$

Then the coefficients a_i of the quartic

$$a_0x^4+4a_1x^3+6a_2x^2+4a_3x+a_4 \quad . \quad . \quad (2)$$

satisfy the recurrence relation (1), which is the recurrence relation used also in the case of the cubic in **56**. These three equations for u and v can be simultaneously true only if

$$J = \begin{vmatrix} a_0 & a_1 & a_2 \\ a_1 & a_2 & a_3 \\ a_2 & a_3 & a_4 \end{vmatrix} = 0. \quad . \quad . \quad . \quad (3)$$

In addition to all the results of **56** (11), p. 128, we now have $p\alpha^4+q\beta^4 = a_4$. Hence

$$a_0x^4+4a_1x^3+6a_2x^2+4a_3x+a_4 = p(x-\alpha)^4+q(x-\beta)^4. \quad (4)$$

This shows that when J vanishes, the quartic is expressible as the sum of two perfect fourth powers, and conversely.

The determinant $| a_0a_2a_4...a_{2n} |$ of the $2n$-ic form

$$a_0x^{2n}+2na_1x^{2n-1}+(2n)_{(2)}a_2x^{2n-2}+...+a_{2n} \quad . \quad (5)$$

is called the *catalecticant* of the form. In the writings of Cayley and Sylvester such a form was often denoted by

$$(a_0, a_1, ..., a_{2n} \between x, 1)^{2n} \quad . \quad . \quad . \quad (6)$$

If the catalecticant vanishes the form, or *quantic*, is expressible as the sum of n perfect $2n$th powers of linear forms $x-\alpha$, each with a constant coefficient, where α is a root of the equation

$$| a_0a_2...a_{2n-2}(-x)^n | = 0, \quad . \quad . \quad (7)$$

the last row in this determinant being understood to be $1, -x, x^2, ..., (-x)^n$, the first row being $a_0, a_1, ..., a_n$.

Next consider the quadratic

$$F \equiv (a+\lambda a')x^2+2(h+\lambda h')x+b+\lambda b'. \quad . \quad (8)$$

It is a perfect square when

$$(a+\lambda a')(b+\lambda b')-(h+\lambda h')^2 = 0, \quad . \quad . \quad (9)$$

where (9) is a quadratic for λ in terms of the other quantities. It follows in general that, for two values λ_1 and λ_2 of λ, we can write the quadratic F in the form $p(x-\alpha)^2$. Accordingly, let

$$f = ax^2+2hx+b, \quad f' = a'x^2+2h'x+b',$$

and $$f+\lambda_1 f' = p(x-\alpha)^2, \quad f+\lambda_2 f' = q(x-\beta)^2. \quad . \quad (10)$$

On solving these two relations for f and f' we obtain

$$f = r(x-\alpha)^2+s(x-\beta)^2, f' = r'(x-\alpha)^2+s'(x-\beta)^2, . \quad (11)$$

where r, s, r', s' are suitable constants.

Again, since a quartic can always be resolved into two quadratic factors f and f', in three ways, we can reduce such a pair of quadratic forms to the present form, and thus express their product, the quartic, as

$$A(x-\alpha)^4+6H(x-\alpha)^2(x-\beta)^2+B(x-\beta)^4, \quad . \quad (12)$$

where $A = rr'$, $6H = rs'+r's$, $B = ss'$.

This is the usual canonical form for a general quartic —the sum of two fourth powers and the product of their squares, with constant coefficients. Evidently our earlier case, where J was zero, corresponds to the possibility that the coefficient H may vanish.

This canonical reduction of the quartic typifies also the reduction for the general $2n$-ic; namely, that the general $2n$-ic can be expressed as the sum of n perfect $2n$th powers of linear forms, affected by constant coefficients, together with a term involving the square of the product of these forms.

61. Gregory's (1675) Method of Solving a Cubic or a Quartic Equation. Let us consider the equation

$$x^3+qx+r = 0.$$

Put $x = z+v$,

so that $$v^3+3zv^2+(3z^2+q)v+z^3+qz+r = 0. \quad . \quad (1)$$

Now multiply this cubic by the arbitrary cubic

$$v^3+av^2+bv+c \quad . \quad . \quad . \quad (2)$$

and in the resulting sextic for v equate to zero the coefficients of v^5, v^4, v^2, v.

Then $3z+a = 0$, $3z^2+q+3za+b = 0$,

$$az^3+aqz+ar+3bz^2+bq+3zc = 0,$$
$$bz^3+bqr+br+3z^2c+qc = 0. \quad (3)$$

Solve these equations for a, b, c in succession.

Then $a = -3z$, $b = 6z^2-q$, and $c = (q^2+3zr-15z^4)/3z$.

Substitute in the final equation and we find that

$$27z^6-27z^3r-q^3 = 0. \qquad (4)$$

This is a quadratic for z^3, whence z is found, and, with it, a, b and c. The sextic for v is of the form $v^6+Av^3+B = 0$, which can now be solved. Finally, $x = z+v$.

Next consider the quartic $x^4+qx^2+rx+s = 0$, with $x = z+v$, so that

$$v^4+4zv^3+(6z^2+q)v^2+(4z^3+2qz+r)v+z^4+qz^2+rz+s = 0. \quad (5)$$

Multiply this by the arbitrary quadratic v^2+av+b, choosing a and b such that the resulting sextic in v may have no term in v^5 or v^3 or v.

Then $4z+a = 0$, $4z^3+2qz+r+6z^2a+qa+4bz = 0$,

$$a(z^4+qz^2+rz+s)+b(4z^3+2qz+r) = 0. \quad (6)$$

Hence $a = -4z$, $b = (20z^3+2qz-r)/4z$

and $$64z^6+32qz^4+(4q^2-16s)z^2-r^2 = 0. \quad (7)$$

Solve this cubic for z^2, whence z, a, b are found. Next solve the sextic for v, which is of the form

$$v^6+Av^4+Bv^2+C = 0,$$

and so is a cubic in v^2. Finally, $x = z+v$.

Next, the quintic equation, $x^5+qx^3+rx^2+sx+t = 0$. Gregory put $x = z+v$ as before, and multiplied the quintic in v by an arbitrary form $v^{15}+av^{14}+\ldots+k$ of degree 15. He equated every coefficient in the resulting 20-ic to zero, except those belonging to v^{20}, v^{15}, v^{10}, v^5, v^0. This gave him sixteen equations for the fifteen unknown coefficients a, b, ..., k and for z. *If they could be solved*, then v^5 would depend on a quartic and the value of x would be found.

Death intervened (in 1675) before he had completed the full investigation. Actually the eliminations would have led to a *sextic* equation for a power of z, but the matter was not cleared up until the time of Abel early in the nineteenth century. So sure was Gregory that he had discovered the general algebraic method of solving all equations that he was in correspondence with his friends Collins and Dary, arranging for the calculation of the eliminations for all equations up to the tenth degree !

Abel proved that the resolvent of any equation of degree $n>4$ was an equation of degree *higher* than n ; and this epoch-making result established the impossibility of solving general algebraic equations of the fifth or higher degree by rational processes and explicit root extractions in a finite number of steps.

Examples.

1. Solve (i) $x^4+2x^3-14x^2+8 = 0$.
(ii) $6x^4-x^2-x+1 = 0$.

2. If $\alpha+\beta=\gamma+\delta$ for the general quartic, prove that $a_0^2a_3-3a_0a_1a_2+2a_1^3 = 0$.

Solve $x^4-8x^3+8x^2+32x-44 = 0$.

3. Solve $\begin{vmatrix} x & a & b & c \\ a & x & . & . \\ b & . & x & . \\ c & . & . & x \end{vmatrix} = 0, \quad \begin{vmatrix} x & 1 & . & . \\ 1 & 2x & 1 & . \\ . & 1 & 2x & 1 \\ . & . & 1 & 2x \end{vmatrix} = 0.$

The latter determinant is $\cos 4\theta$ if $x = \cos\theta$; hence $x = \cos\frac{r\pi}{8}$, $r = 1, 3, 5, 7$. Generalize.

4. Express the discriminant of a cubic or a biquadratic as a determinant in the s_i (p. 80).

5. The following alternative form of Ferrari's method is useful in solving numerical examples.

Solve $x^4+4x^3+8x^2+7x+4 = 0$.

Let this equation be written

$$(x^2+2x+t)^2 = (ax+b)^2.$$

Then, on comparing coefficients,

$$2t-a^2 = 4, \quad 4t-2ab = 7, \quad t^2-b^2 = 4.$$

Whence $4(2t-4)(t^2-4) = 4a^2b^2 = (4t-7)^2$,

so that $8t^3-32t^2+24t+15 = 0$.

A rational factor of this cubic is $2t-5$, yielding $t = 2\frac{1}{2}$, $a = \pm 1$, $b = \pm 1\frac{1}{2}$, and leading to rational quadratic factors $(x^2+x+1)(x^2+3x+4)$ of the quartic.

CHAPTER XI

ELIMINATION OF THE UNKNOWN FROM CONSISTENT EQUATIONS

62. Dialytic Elimination. From n separate equations it is generally possible to eliminate $n-1$ unknowns. The following, which is called by Sylvester the *dialytic* method, provides a systematic means of eliminating one unknown from two equations. From the reverse point of view the vanishing of the eliminant may be regarded as the condition under which the two equations in question possess a common root.

Consider the case

$$ax^3+bx^2+cx+d = 0, \quad px^2+qx+r = 0. \quad . \quad (1)$$

Multiply the cubic by x, and the quadratic by x and also by x^2, so that five relations are obtained :

$$\begin{aligned} ax^4+bx^3+cx^2+dx \quad &= 0,\\ ax^3+bx^2+cx+d &= 0,\\ px^2+qx+r &= 0,\\ px^3+qx^2+rx \quad &= 0,\\ px^4+qx^3+rx^2 \quad &= 0. \end{aligned} \quad . \quad . \quad (2)$$

If we treat these as five linear equations, homogeneous in x^4, x^3, x^2, x, 1, the condition for their consistency is, by the theory of linear equations (Aitken, *Determinants and Matrices*, p. 64),

$$|R| \equiv \begin{vmatrix} a & b & c & d & . \\ . & a & b & c & d \\ . & . & p & q & r \\ . & p & q & r & . \\ p & q & r & . & . \end{vmatrix} = 0. \quad . \quad . \quad (3)$$

Since the term involving a^2 in the expanded form of this determinant $|R|$ is easily seen to be $-a^2r^3$, the expansion does not vanish identically. But it is free from x: hence it is the required eliminant, or *resultant*.

Similar methods apply to a pair of equations of degrees m and n: corresponding to the m-ic there are n rows in the determinant, corresponding to the n-ic there are m rows. In all there are $m+n$ rows. This type of determinant is usually called (Aitken, *Determinants and Matrices*, p. 125) a *bigradient*.

From three equations, consistent in two unknowns x and y, we could eliminate x from the first and second, and again from the first and third equation, giving two resultants containing y, from which y could be eliminated by a like procedure.

63. Factorized Form of the Resultant. Suppose that we have

$$\begin{aligned} ax^3+bx^2+cx+d &= a(x-\alpha)(x-\beta)(x-\gamma) = f(x), \\ px^2+qx+r &= p(x-\lambda)(x-\mu) \qquad\quad = \phi(x). \end{aligned} \quad . \quad (1)$$

Then, when both $f(x)$ and $\phi(x)$ vanish simultaneously, one of λ, μ must equal one of α, β or γ; and so the following relation must exist:

$$|R'| \equiv (\lambda-\alpha)(\lambda-\beta)(\lambda-\gamma)(\mu-\alpha)(\mu-\beta)(\mu-\gamma) = 0. \quad (2)$$

This can be written in terms of alternants (p. 47) as

$$\Delta(\lambda\mu\alpha\beta\gamma)/\Delta(\lambda\mu)\Delta(\alpha\beta\gamma) = 0, \quad . \quad . \quad . \quad (3)$$

or again, since $f(\lambda) = a(\lambda-\alpha)(\lambda-\beta)(\lambda-\gamma)$, and so on,

$$p^3a^2|R'| = p^3f(\lambda)f(\mu) = a^2\phi(\alpha)\phi(\beta)\phi(\gamma) = 0. \quad . \quad (4)$$

We have evidently hit upon several alternative forms of resultant for f and ϕ, and the question arises, how are these related to the bigradient $|R|$? The answer is as follows:—

By row-into-column multiplication we have

$$\begin{bmatrix} a & b & c & d & . \\ . & a & b & c & d \\ . & . & p & q & r \\ . & p & q & r & . \\ p & q & r & . & . \end{bmatrix} \begin{bmatrix} \alpha^4 & \beta^4 & \gamma^4 & \lambda^4 & \mu^4 \\ \alpha^3 & \beta^3 & \gamma^3 & \lambda^3 & \mu^3 \\ \alpha^2 & \beta^2 & \gamma^2 & \lambda^2 & \mu^2 \\ \alpha & \beta & \gamma & \lambda & \mu \\ 1 & 1 & 1 & 1 & 1 \end{bmatrix} = \begin{bmatrix} . & . & . & \lambda f_\lambda & \mu f_\mu \\ . & . & . & f_\lambda & f_\mu \\ \phi_\alpha & \phi_\beta & \phi_\gamma & . & . \\ \alpha\phi_\alpha & \beta\phi_\beta & \gamma\phi_\gamma & . & . \\ \alpha^2\phi_\alpha & \beta^2\phi_\beta & \gamma^2\phi_\gamma & . & . \end{bmatrix} \quad (5)$$

where $f_\lambda \equiv f(\lambda)$, $\phi_\alpha \equiv \phi(\alpha)$, etc. On taking determinants we have

$$|R||R'|\Delta(\alpha\beta\gamma)\Delta(\lambda\mu) = -f_\lambda f_\mu \phi_\alpha \phi_\beta \phi_\gamma \Delta(\alpha\beta\gamma)\Delta(\lambda\mu). \quad . \quad (6)$$

But $|R'| = f_\lambda f_\mu / a^2 = \phi_\alpha \phi_\beta \phi_\gamma / p^3$.

Hence $|R||R'| = -a^2p^3|R'|^2$, or $|R| = -a^2p^3|R'|$. . (7)

The alternative forms of the resultant $|R| = 0$, $|R'| = 0$ are therefore clearly equivalent, as was pointed out by Professor E. T. Whittaker (*Proc. Edin. Math. Soc.*, Series 1, vol. **40** (1922), pp. 62-63) who gave a proof substantially the same as the above.

64. Bézout's Condensed Eliminant. In 1779 Bézout gave a method which produces an n-rowed determinant as the eliminant of two equations of degree n. For example, consider the case $n = 3$ for two cubics

$$\begin{aligned} f(x) &= a_0x^3 + a_1x^2 + a_2x + a_3 = 0, \\ \phi(x) &= b_0x^3 + b_1x^2 + b_2x + b_3 = 0. \end{aligned} \quad . \quad . \quad (1)$$

Multiply these two equations successively by

$$\begin{aligned} b_0 &\text{ and } a_0 \text{ respectively,} \\ b_0x + b_1 &\text{ and } a_0x + a_1, \\ b_0x^2 + b_1x + b_2 &\text{ and } a_0x^2 + a_1x + a_2, \end{aligned}$$

and subtract each time the products so formed. Then the results are the three following equations :

$$\begin{aligned} |a_0b_1|x^2 &+ |a_0b_2|x + |a_0b_3| = 0, \\ |a_0b_2|x^2 &+ (|a_0b_3| + |a_1b_2|)x + |a_1b_3| = 0, \\ |a_0b_3|x^2 &+ |a_1b_3|x + |a_2b_3| = 0. \end{aligned} \quad . \quad (2)$$

where $|a_0b_1|$ represents the determinant $\begin{vmatrix} a_0 & a_1 \\ b_0 & b_1 \end{vmatrix}$, and so on.

By eliminating from these three equations x^2, x as distinct variables, we obtain the resultant as a three-rowed determinant equated to zero, thus,

$$\begin{vmatrix} |a_0b_1| & |a_0b_2| & |a_0b_3| \\ |a_0b_2| & |a_0b_3|+|a_1b_2| & |a_1b_3| \\ |a_0b_3| & |a_1b_3| & |a_2b_3| \end{vmatrix} = 0. \quad . \quad . \quad (3)$$

This determinant is called Bézout's eliminant, sometimes the *Bezoutian* or *Bezoutiant.* The case for a general value of n is constructed in similar fashion.

65. Relation between the Dialytic Eliminant and Bézout's Eliminant. Taking first for illustration the case $m = n = 3$, let us consider the bigradient resultant matrix

$$R = \begin{bmatrix} a_0 & a_1 & a_2 & a_3 & . & . \\ . & a_0 & a_1 & a_2 & a_3 & . \\ . & . & a_0 & a_1 & a_2 & a_3 \\ . & . & b_0 & b_1 & b_2 & b_3 \\ . & b_0 & b_1 & b_2 & b_3 & . \\ b_0 & b_1 & b_2 & b_3 & . & . \end{bmatrix} \quad . \quad . \quad (1)$$

Premultiply R (in ordinary matrical, or row-into-column, multiplication) by a suitably partitioned matrix

$$K = \begin{bmatrix} 1 & . & . & . & . & . \\ . & 1 & . & . & . & . \\ . & . & 1 & . & . & . \\ . & . & -b_0 & a_0 & . & . \\ . & -b_0 & -b_1 & a_1 & a_0 & . \\ -b_0 & -b_1 & -b_2 & a_2 & a_1 & a_0 \end{bmatrix} \quad . \quad . \quad (2)$$

The result is

$$KR = \begin{bmatrix} a_0 & a_1 & a_2 & a_3 & \cdot & \cdot \\ \cdot & a_0 & a_1 & a_2 & a_3 & \cdot \\ \cdot & \cdot & a_0 & a_1 & a_2 & a_3 \\ \cdot & \cdot & \cdot & |a_0b_1| & |a_0b_2| & |a_0b_3| \\ \cdot & \cdot & \cdot & |a_0b_2| & |a_0b_3|+|a_1b_2| & |a_1b_3| \\ \cdot & \cdot & \cdot & |a_0b_3| & |a_1b_3| & |a_2b_3| \end{bmatrix}. \quad . \quad (3)$$

The determinant $|K|$ of K is evidently a_0^3, and the determinant $|KR|$ is likewise evidently a_0^3 multiplied by the three-rowed determinant of the elements in the lower right-hand corner. Hence, by taking determinants of both sides and cancelling a_0^3, we have

$$|R| = \begin{vmatrix} |a_0b_1| & |a_0b_2| & |a_0b_3| \\ |a_0b_2| & |a_0b_3|+|a_1b_2| & |a_1b_3| \\ |a_0b_3| & |a_1b_3| & |a_2b_3| \end{vmatrix} \quad . \quad . \quad (4)$$

which shows that the bigradient and the Bezoutian eliminants are identical in value.

The elements of the Bezoutian contain minors of the 2nd order and of weight (in the (i, j)th element) $i+j-1$, these minors being taken from the rectangular two-rowed matrix

$$\begin{bmatrix} a_0 & a_1 & a_2 & \dots & a_n \\ b_0 & b_1 & b_2 & \dots & b_n \end{bmatrix} \quad . \quad . \quad . \quad (5)$$

this last matrix being most obviously connected with the identity

$$\begin{bmatrix} a_0 & a_1 & a_2 & \dots & a_n \\ b_0 & b_1 & b_2 & \dots & b_n \end{bmatrix} \begin{bmatrix} \alpha^n \\ \alpha^{n-1} \\ \alpha^{n-2} \\ \vdots \\ 1 \end{bmatrix} = \begin{bmatrix} 0 \\ 0 \end{bmatrix}, \quad . \quad (6)$$

where α is a common root of the associated equations which give rise to the eliminant.

66. Case of Quantics of Unequal Degrees. As for the case when $m>n$, it is easily derivable. In the transformation KR of **65**, put $b_0 = 0$, and then alter $[b_1\ b_2\ b_3]$ to $[b_0\ b_1\ b_2]$. This gives

$$|R| = \begin{vmatrix} a_0 & a_1 & a_2 & a_3 & \cdot \\ \cdot & a_0 & a_1 & a_2 & a_3 \\ \cdot & \cdot & b_0 & b_1 & b_2 \\ \cdot & b_0 & b_1 & b_2 & \cdot \\ b_0 & b_1 & b_2 & \cdot & \cdot \end{vmatrix} = \begin{vmatrix} b_0 & b_1 & b_2 \\ a_0b_1 & a_0b_2+|a_1b_1| & |a_1b_2| \\ a_0b_2 & |a_1b_2| & |a_2b_2| \end{vmatrix} \quad . \quad (1)$$

where the elements in the second and third rows are to be regarded as minors of the array or matrix

$$\begin{bmatrix} a_0 & a_1 & a_2 & a_3 \\ \cdot & b_0 & b_1 & b_2 \end{bmatrix} \quad . \quad . \quad . \quad (2)$$

If we introduce a factor a_0 and write the top row of the eliminant as $[a_0b_0,\ a_0b_1,\ a_0b_2]$ the result is more symmetrical, while it still gives a genuine eliminant, since $a_0 \neq 0$.

For the general case, where $m-n = r$, we take the fundamental array to be

$$\begin{bmatrix} a_0 & a_1 & a_2 & \dots & a_r & a_{r+1} & \dots & a_m \\ \cdot & \cdot & \cdot & \dots & b_0 & b_1 & \dots & b_n \end{bmatrix} \quad . \quad . \quad . \quad (3)$$

by putting the first r coefficients b_j in **65** (5) equal to zero and renaming the suffixes of the remaining b_j so that they become $b_0, b_1, \dots, b_n$.

Examples. 1. Obtain the dialytic and the Bezoutian form of the eliminant of (i) two quadratics, (ii) two quartics, (iii) a quadratic and a quartic.

2. If $f(x)$ and $g(x)$ are polynomials, prove that

$$\{f(x)g(y)-f(y)g(x)\}/(x-y)$$

is also a polynomial.

3. Write out this derived polynomial of Ex. 2 in powers of y, when $f(x)$ is a cubic and $g(x)$ a quadratic. By equating coefficients of powers of y to zero, and then eliminating

powers of x in the results, obtain the Bezoutian eliminant of $f(x)$ and $g(x)$.

4. Derive on the model of Ex. 3 an alternative method for obtaining the Bezoutian eliminant of two equations.

67. Elimination and the G.C.M. Process. Still another way of obtaining the resultant $|R|$ of two polynomials $f(x)$ and $\phi(x)$ is to perform the Euclidean G.C.M. process upon them. For example, if $f(x)$ and $\phi(x)$ are the cubics given in the equations **64** (1), the process begins with dividing $\phi(x)$ by $f(x)$. To avoid fractions, multiply $\phi(x)$ by the non-zero constant a_0: then the first quotient is b_0 and the remainder a quadratic whose leading term is $|a_0b_1|x^2$. Before the next division multiply the dividend by $|a_0b_1|$, again to avoid fractions, and continue in the same way. If f and ϕ have no common factor involving x the remainder will be a constant $|R|$, a polynomial expression in the coefficients a_j and b_j. As in **17**, p. 38, we shall have an identity

$$Af+B\phi = |R|. \quad . \quad . \quad . \quad (1)$$

Now if the equations **64** (1) are simultaneously true when $x = \alpha$, then $f = \phi = 0$ at this value of x and hence $|R| = 0$. But $|R|$ is independent of x: hence $|R| = 0$ for all values of x and is in fact the same resultant as before. Conversely, if $|R|$ does not vanish it is impossible for f and ϕ to have a common factor.

This method gives the necessary and sufficient condition for f and ϕ to have not only one root in common but also k roots in common. For if the intermediate remainder which is of degree k in x does not vanish identically while the next, which would usually be of degree $k-1$, does vanish identically, then the G.C.M. is of degree k, and exactly k roots are common to f and ϕ. The condition is therefore given by equating each of the k coefficients of powers of x in this remainder to zero.

It is interesting to know that all these remainders can

be given in dialytic form through a formula due to Cayley (1848). For two cubics, **64** (3), it is

$$|R| = \begin{vmatrix} a_0 & a_1 & a_2 & a_3 & . & x^2f(x) \\ . & a_0 & a_1 & a_2 & a_3 & xf(x) \\ . & . & a_0 & a_1 & a_2 & f(x) \\ . & . & b_0 & b_1 & b_2 & \phi(x) \\ . & b_0 & b_1 & b_2 & b_3 & x\phi(x) \\ b_0 & b_1 & b_2 & b_3 & . & x^2\phi(x) \end{vmatrix} \quad . \quad . \quad (2)$$

Here the sixth column can at once be reduced to

$$\{ . \; . \; a_3 \; b_3 \; . \; . \}$$

by subtracting x^5 col_1, and so on : hence $|R|$ is the dialytic eliminant of Sylvester. Delete row_1, row_6, col_1, col_5 from $|R|$ and the resulting four-rowed minor gives the penultimate remainder $|S|$. Delete row_1, row_4, col_1, col_3 of $|S|$ and the first remainder is obtained. For a full discussion see Muir, *History of Determinants* (1920), vol. 3, pp. 329-349, which comments on Trudi's paper of 1862.

Miscellaneous Examples

1. Between what values must the quantity m lie if the roots of the equation

$$x^2+2x(m+5)+2m^2+11m+23=0$$

are to be real ?

2. Draw the graphs of x^2 and of $8-x^3$, and hence find approximately the real root of the equation $x^3+x^2-8=0$.

3. Find the equation whose roots are the squares of those of $x^3+x+1=0$.

4. If $f(x)$ is a polynomial of order n in x, prove $f(x)f(-x)$ is one of order n in x^2.

5. If $y=x^2$, and $f(x)f(-x) = \phi(y)$, what are the roots of $\phi(y) = 0$? [The squares of those of x.

6. Solve $27x^4-45x^2+28x-4=0$, which has a repeated root. $\left[\frac{2}{3}, \frac{2}{3}, \frac{-2\pm\sqrt{7}}{3}.\right.$

7. Solve $x^3-6x^2+9x = 3$ by taking $x = 2+2\cos\theta$. Prove that one root is $4\cos^2 10^0$ and find the other roots.

8. The sextic equation, $x^6+ax^3+bx+c = 0$, has three roots equal to α. Prove that $c = -5\alpha^6$. Find also a and b in terms of α, and the cubic equation which gives the other three roots.

9. If α is a root of $x^3 = 2$, show that $1+\alpha+\alpha^2$ is a root of $y^3-3y^2-3y-1 = 0$, and solve the latter equation.

10. Determine the nature of the roots of

$$\text{(i) } 3x^3+x^2-11x+6 = 0,$$
$$\text{(ii) } 2x^3+3x = 4,$$

and evaluate their real roots to three significant figures.

11. Complete the solution by Cardan's method for the equation $x^3+12x-112 = 0$ by assuming that $7\pm5\sqrt{2} = (\alpha\pm\beta\sqrt{2})^3$, where α and β are integers:

$$[\alpha = \beta = 1, x = 4; \text{ etc.}]$$

12. Prove that there cannot be two differing identities $S = \phi(e)$, $S = \psi(e)$ expressing S, a given polynomial symmetric function of the roots $x_1, x_2 \ldots, x_n$ as a polynomial in their elementary symmetric functions $e_1 = \Sigma x_i$, $e_2 = \Sigma x_i x_j$, $\ldots, e_n = x_1 x_2 \ldots x_n$.

By subtraction this would imply a nonzero polynomial $F(e)$ in the e's, which would vanish identically when expressed in terms of the x's. Let $T = \lambda e_1{}^p e_2{}^q e_3{}^r \ldots$ be any nonzero term of $F(e)$; that is $\lambda \neq 0$. Expressed in terms of x's let each term T be arranged in descending lexical order with regard to $x_1, x_2, \ldots, x_n$. Then T will necessarily contain a leading term $X = \lambda x_1{}^P x_2{}^Q x_3{}^R \ldots$, where $P = p+q+r+\ldots$, $Q = q+r+\ldots$ $R = r+\ldots$, etc.

Since $p, q, r, \ldots$ are fixed uniquely if $P, Q, R, \ldots$ are given, no two terms T can have the same leading term. Put the leading terms X, one from each T, also into descending lexical order. Since they all differ they too have a single leading term. This term therefore stands foremost of all the terms in x among all the terms T. Hence it is unique and cannot possibly cancel out from the assumed identity; which is absurd. Thus no such identity exists, and the reduction of p. 75 is unique.

CHAPTER XII

FURTHER LIMITING AND APPROXIMATE PROCESSES

68. Explicit Formulæ for the Roots of Equations. Consider the polynomial F of the nth order, as given on p. 71, where

$$F(x)=(1-\alpha x)(1-\beta x)\ldots(1-\lambda x)=1-e_1x+\ldots+(-)^n e_n x^n, \quad (1)$$

and $1/F(x) = h_0+h_1x+h_2x^2+\ldots$

Multiply this last relation throughout by x^{n-1} and use (1) p. 47. Then we find that the left-hand side expression yields

$$\frac{x^{n-1}}{F(x)} = \begin{vmatrix} 1 & 1 & \cdots \\ \alpha & \beta & \cdots \\ \cdots & \cdots & \cdots \\ \alpha^{n-2} & \beta^{n-2} & \cdots \\ (1-\alpha x)^{-1} & (1-\beta x)^{-1} & \cdots \end{vmatrix} \div \begin{vmatrix} 1 & 1 & \cdots\cdots \\ \alpha & \beta & \cdots\cdots \\ \cdots & \cdots & \cdots \\ \alpha^{n-2} & \beta^{n-2} & \cdots\cdots \\ \alpha^{n-1} & \beta^{n-1} & \cdots\cdots \end{vmatrix} \quad (2)$$

while h_r is now the coefficient of x^{n+r-1} on the right. Expand each of the n elements in the bottom row of this numerator determinant in ascending powers of x (as in (2) p. 70). Since x^p occurs in the lowest row only of this determinant and then along with α^p etc., the coefficient of x^p on the right has for numerator the n-rowed determinant

$$\begin{vmatrix} 1 & 1 & \cdots\cdots \\ \alpha & \beta & \cdots\cdots \\ \cdots & \cdots & \cdots \\ \alpha^{n-2} & \beta^{n-2} & \cdots\cdots \\ \alpha^{p} & \beta^{p} & \cdots\cdots \end{vmatrix} \equiv A(0, 1, \ldots, n-2, p) \quad . \quad (3)$$

say, while the denominator is a particular case of this with $p = n-1$. For lower positive integral and zero values of p this *alternant* A vanishes identically, having two equal rows. For higher values it duly gives the h expressions in *bialternant* form

$$h_r = A(0, 1, 2, \ldots, n-2, n+r-1)/A(0, 1, 2, \ldots, n-1) \quad (4)$$

Example.

$$\text{For a cubic, } h_5 = \begin{vmatrix} 1 & 1 & 1 \\ \alpha & \beta & \gamma \\ \alpha^7 & \beta^7 & \gamma^7 \end{vmatrix} \div \begin{vmatrix} 1 & 1 & 1 \\ \alpha & \beta & \gamma \\ \alpha^2 & \beta^2 & \gamma^2 \end{vmatrix} = \frac{A(017)}{A(012)}.$$

Now suppose that among the n real or complex roots α, β, ... the modulus $|\alpha|$ of α exceeds that of each of the rest. Then it follows that the ratio h_{r+1}/h_r tends to α itself as r tends to infinity. For since $|\alpha|>|\beta|$, therefore $|\beta/\alpha|^r \to 0$. Hence $\beta^r/\alpha^r \to 0$ also, and likewise for each further root compared with α. On dividing each element of the bottom row in the numerator of both h_{r+1} and h_r by α^r and then proceeding to the limit, the result follows. Thus, with $n = 3$,

$$\frac{h_{r+1}}{h_r} = \frac{A(0, 1, r+3)/A(012)}{A(0, 1, r+2)/A(012)} \to \begin{vmatrix} 1 & 1 & 1 \\ \alpha & \beta & \gamma \\ \alpha^3 & 0 & 0 \end{vmatrix} \div \begin{vmatrix} 1 & 1 & 1 \\ \alpha & \beta & \gamma \\ \alpha^2 & 0 & 0 \end{vmatrix}$$

$$= \frac{\alpha^3 B(01)}{\alpha^2 B(01)} = \alpha, \quad . \quad . \quad . \quad . \quad . \quad (5)$$

where $B(01)$ denotes the two-rowed alternant of β, γ. Similarly for n in general.

The same property holds in the confluent case provided that α is a repeated root whose modulus again exceeds that of each of the rest. Suitable confluent determinants now appear in (2) as they did on p. 48. Thus if α is repeated exactly k times, the first k columns in both these determinants belong to α. The preceding argument for the limit then clears the bottom row of each determinant as before, except in these first k columns. Further division of these bottom rows by r^{k-1}, before taking the limit, leads to zeros in all but the kth column of each determinant, and to the result α as before. Thus, with $n = 3$ and just two equal roots,

$$\frac{h_{r+1}}{h_r} = \begin{vmatrix} 1 & . & 1 \\ \alpha & 1 & \gamma \\ \alpha^{r+3} & (r+3)\alpha^{r+2} & \gamma^{r+3} \end{vmatrix} \div \begin{vmatrix} 1 & . & 1 \\ \alpha & 1 & \gamma \\ \alpha^{r+2} & (r+2)\alpha^{r+1} & \gamma^{r+2} \end{vmatrix}$$

$$\rightarrow \begin{vmatrix} 1 & . & 1 \\ \alpha & 1 & \gamma \\ . & \alpha^2 & . \end{vmatrix} \div \begin{vmatrix} 1 & . & . \\ \alpha & 1 & \gamma \\ . & \alpha & . \end{vmatrix} = \alpha \quad . \quad . \quad . \quad (6)$$

This has proved the following theorem :

Theorem. When the modulus of one root, repeated or unrepeated, exceeds that of each of the remaining roots, then the ratio h_{r+1}/h_r *tends to this root for its limit as* r *tends to infinity.*

Let us call this the *regular* case, and denote all others, where the greatest modulus belongs to two or more distinct roots, as *irregular*. Evidently these last include the case when the greatest modulus belongs to a complex root (and therefore to its differing conjugate complex root) in a real equation. Two theorems for the regular case can now be proved. The first is a simplified form of one by Daniel Bernoulli (1728): the second, which marks an epoch in the long history of equations by giving an explicit formula for a root, was discovered by E. T. Whittaker in 1918 (*Proc. Edin. Math. Soc.* 1, **36** (1918) p. 103).

Corollary. By an algebraical, followed by an arithmetical, division the root with greatest modulus, in the regular case, can be found to any degree of accuracy.

Proof. Divide unity by $F(x)$, using algebraical long division, and so obtain consecutive coefficients h_r, h_{r+1}, ... in the quotient. (As in Horner's method there is no need to write down the letter x, only the numerical values of the terms.) At any suitable stage divide h_{r+1} by h_r, and the resulting quotient is an approximation to such a root, by the preceding theorem.

Examples.

1. If $F(x) = 1-9x-10x^2+11x^3$, the h series is 1, 9, 91, 898, 8893, 88016, ... by long division. Also $88016 \div 8893 = 9\cdot897...$, within $\cdot001$ of a. Horner's method gives $9\cdot898...$.

2. Prove that the theorem holds even when any finite polynomial replaces unity in the numerator. What happens if this numerator contains a factor in common with the denominator?

Whittaker's Theorem. If the equation

$$0 = e_0 - e_1x + e_2x^2 - e_3x^3 + e_4x^4 - \dots, \quad (e_0 = 1)$$

has a root a^{-1} which is smallest in absolute value, then

$$\frac{1}{a} = \frac{e_0}{e_1} + \frac{e_2}{e_1\begin{vmatrix} e_1 & e_2 \\ e_0 & e_1 \end{vmatrix}} + \frac{\begin{vmatrix} e_2 & e_3 \\ e_1 & e_2 \end{vmatrix}}{\begin{vmatrix} e_1 & e_2 \\ e_0 & e_1 \end{vmatrix}\begin{vmatrix} e_1 & e_2 & e_3 \\ e_0 & e_1 & e_2 \\ \cdot & e_0 & e_1 \end{vmatrix}} + \dots \quad . \quad . \quad (7)$$

provided that the series converges.

Proof. Let this series be written in the notation

$$\frac{e_0}{e_1} + \frac{e_2}{e_1\,e_{11}} + \frac{e_{22}}{e_{11}\,e_{111}} + \frac{e_{222}}{e_{111}\,e_{1111}} + \dots \quad . \quad . \quad (8)$$

where the rule of suffix formation is obvious, and the connexion between multiple suffix and the corresponding determinant is defined by the relation

$$e_{pqr\dots} = \begin{vmatrix} e_p & e_{q+1} & e_{r+2} & \cdots \\ e_{p-1} & e_q & e_{r+1} & \cdots \\ e_{p-2} & e_{q-1} & e_r & \cdots \\ \cdots & \cdots & \cdots & \cdots \end{vmatrix}, \; 0 \leqslant p \leqslant q \leqslant r \leqslant \dots . \quad (9)$$

The principal diagonal e_p, e_q, e_r, ... of the determinant is at once fixed by the multiple suffix in $e_{pqr}\dots$. Each column is characterized by descending and consecutive suffixes.

At present we shall only need the case when all suffixes p, q, r are equal within a multiple suffix. As in the first column of e_{111} above, negative suffixes cannot occur: instead, zero elements appear.

By a theorem on dual bialternants (Aitken, *Determinants and Matrices*, p. 117) we have the identity

$$e_{pqr}\ldots = h_{\pi\rho}\ldots \qquad . \quad . \quad . \quad (10)$$

where $\{pqr\ldots\}$ and $\{\pi\rho\ldots\}$ are conjugate partitions (p. 2) of the same positive integer, and $h_{\pi\rho}\ldots$ is constructed analogously to the determinant (9). Simple instances of this have occurred at (2) p. 71, which yield $e_1 = h_1$, $e_2 = h_{11}$, $h_2 = e_{11}$, $h_3 = e_{111}$ etc. The graph, as on p. 2, shows that $e_{22} = h_{22}$ and $e_{222} = h_{33}$. On translating from e to h the first r terms of the series (8) now become

$$\frac{h_0}{h_1} + \frac{h_{11}}{h_1h_2} + \frac{h_{22}}{h_2h_3} + \ldots + \frac{h_{r-1,\, r-1}}{h_{r-1}\, h_r}$$
$$= \frac{h_0}{h_1} + \left(\frac{h_1}{h_2} - \frac{h_0}{h_1}\right) + \left(\frac{h_2}{h_3} - \frac{h_1}{h_2}\right) + \ldots + \left(\frac{h_{r-1}}{h_r} - \frac{h_{r-2}}{h_{r-1}}\right)$$
$$= h_{r-1}/h_r.$$

But this tends to a^{-1} as r tends to infinity, by the Theorem of p. 151, and so proves the theorem.

Corollary. If a finite number of h_i *vanish but all* h_{p+i} $(i>0)$ *are non-zero, after a suitably chosen value* p, *then*

$$\frac{1}{a} = \frac{h_{p-1}}{h_p} + \frac{h_{pp}}{h_p h_{p+1}} + \ldots \qquad . \quad . \quad . \quad (11)$$

This follows by the same methods of proof. We may note that the theorem and corollary cover the regular case. For in this case the limit of h_{r-1}/h_r exists so that only a finite number of terms h_i could vanish. The modified series (11) is automatically convergent.

69. The Irregular Case. In 1924 Aitken * extended this result to give the elementary symmetric functions of a subclass $\alpha^{-1}, \beta^{-1}, \ldots$ of the roots, such that each modulus $|\alpha|, |\beta|, \ldots$ exceeds each modulus of an omitted root. This covers the irregular case wherein several distinct roots in the subclass have the same maximum modulus. Not merely the elementary but all the usual symmetric functions may be derived by such series. They depend on the ratio h_P/h_Q where P and Q are suitably chosen, equally numerous, multiple suffixes.

To illustrate this let $\alpha \neq \beta$, but $|\alpha| = |\beta| > |\gamma|$, where γ denotes any other root. This case of *two* such equal moduli needs the *double* suffix function

$$h_{rr} = \begin{vmatrix} h_r & h_{r+1} \\ h_{r-1} & h_r \end{vmatrix}$$

and the identity $h_r\, h_{rrr} = h_{rr}\, h_{rr} - h_{r-1,\, r-1}\, h_{r+1,\, r+1}$, which arises at once by applying Jacobi's theorem of the adjugate (cf. Aitken, *Determinants*, p. 98) to the cofactors of the four corner-elements in the three-rowed determinant h_{rrr}.

In fact we have

$$\begin{aligned} \frac{h_{rr}}{h_{r+1,\, r+1}} &= \frac{h_0}{h_{11}} + \left(\frac{h_{11}}{h_{22}} - \frac{h_0}{h_{11}}\right) + \ldots + \left(\frac{h_{rr}}{h_{r+1,\, r+1}} - \frac{h_{r-1}\, h_{r-1}}{h_{rr}}\right) \\ &= \frac{h_0}{h_{11}} + \frac{h_1\, h_{111}}{h_{11}\, h_{22}} + \ldots + \frac{h_r\, h_{rrr}}{h_{rr}\, h_{r+1,\, r+1}} \end{aligned}$$

by repeated use of Jacobi's theorem. Also by a Lemma which follows below, the left-hand side expression tends to $1/\alpha\beta$ as $r \to \infty$, while the right yields the infinite series in h or e at pleasure. Thus, in the present example,

$$\frac{1}{\alpha\beta} = \frac{e_0}{e_2} + \frac{e_1\, e_3}{e_2\, e_{22}} + \frac{e_{11}\, e_{33}}{e_{22}\, e_{222}} + \ldots \quad . \quad . \quad . \quad (12)$$

* A. C. Aitken, *Proc. Royal Soc. Edin.*, **45** (1925), p. 14; **46** (1926), p. 289.

From the limit of $h_{r-1,\,r}/h_{rr}$ we may similarly deduce that

$$\frac{1}{\alpha}+\frac{1}{\beta}=\frac{h_1}{h_{11}}+\frac{h_2\,h_{111}}{h_{11}\,h_{22}}+\ldots=\frac{e_1}{e_2}+\frac{e_{11}\,e_3}{e_2\,e_{22}}+\frac{e_{111}\,e_{33}}{e_{22}\,e_{222}}+\ldots \qquad (13)$$

From (12) and (13) the values of α and β can now be found.

Lemma. The limit of $h_{rr}/h_{r+1,\,r+1} = 1/\alpha\beta$ as $r \to \infty$ (14)

Proof. We use Jacobi's fundamental identity for bialternants,

$$h_{pq\ldots r} = A(p, q+1, \ldots, r+n-1)/A(0, 1, \ldots, n-1)\,. \qquad (15)$$

Cf. Aitken, *Determinants*, p. 116. For brevity take $n = 4$, and four distinct roots $\alpha, \beta, \gamma, \delta$. Then

$$\frac{h_{rr}}{h_{r+1,\,r+1}} = \begin{vmatrix} 1 & 1 & 1 & 1 \\ \alpha & \beta & \gamma & \delta \\ \alpha^{r+2} & \beta^{r+2} & \gamma^{r+2} & \delta^{r+2} \\ \alpha^{r+3} & \beta^{r+3} & \gamma^{r+3} & \delta^{r+3} \end{vmatrix} \div \begin{vmatrix} 1 & 1 & 1 & 1 \\ \alpha & \beta & \gamma & \delta \\ \alpha^{r+3} & \beta^{r+3} & \gamma^{r+3} & \delta^{r+3} \\ \alpha^{r+4} & \beta^{r+4} & \gamma^{r+4} & \delta^{r+4} \end{vmatrix}.$$

Expand each determinant by a Laplace development of the top $n-2$ rows with the bottom two rows. Then divide both expansions throughout by $\alpha^r\beta^r$. Since $[(\gamma \text{ or } \delta)\div(\alpha \text{ or } \beta)]^r$ will occur in every term of each expansion, except the first term, the first alone of each will not tend to zero as $r\to\infty$. Hence the quotient tends to

$$\begin{vmatrix} 1 & 1 & 1 & 1 \\ \alpha & \beta & \gamma & \delta \\ \alpha^2 & \beta^2 & . & . \\ \alpha^3 & \beta^3 & . & . \end{vmatrix} \div \begin{vmatrix} 1 & 1 & 1 & 1 \\ \alpha & \beta & \gamma & \delta \\ \alpha^3 & \beta^3 & . & . \\ \alpha^4 & \beta^4 & . & . \end{vmatrix}$$

which reduces to $1/\alpha\beta$. Similarly for (13). The confluent case presents no difficulty if taken as in (6).

Examples.

1. Prove that $\alpha=\dfrac{e_1}{e_0}-\dfrac{e_2}{e_1}-\dfrac{e_{22}}{e_1e_{11}}-\dfrac{e_{222}}{e_{11}e_{111}}-\ldots$ for the greatest $|\alpha|$.

2. Prove that $a^{-2} = \dfrac{e_0}{e_{11}} + \dfrac{e_{12}}{e_{11}e_{111}} + \dfrac{e_{122}}{e_{111}e_{1111}} + \ldots$.

3. If $x^n = e_1x^{n-1} - e_2x^{n-2} + \ldots$, prove that

$$x^{n+p-1} = h_px^{n-1} - h_{p1}x^{n-2} + h_{p11}x^{n-3} - \ldots.$$

[Hints: 1. Use h_{r+1}/h_r. 2. h_r/h_{r+2}]

70. Other Approximate Methods for Solving Equations. For further details on numerical solutions of equations the reader should consult Whittaker and Robinson's *Calculus of Observations* (1926), pp. 78-132. But two more of the early methods may be mentioned here for their simplicity and interest.

Anderson's Method.* To solve $f(x) = 0$ having found a fair approximation $x = a$, put $x = a(1+y)/(1-y)$ so that y is necessarily small. Obtain the corresponding equation for y but neglect third and higher powers of y, say $p+qy+ry^2 = 0$. Then $y = -p/q$ nearly, so that $y = -p/(q+ry) = -p/(q-pr/q)$ more nearly. From this a greatly improved value of x is obtained. The method is powerful and applies to equations algebraical or transcendental, and can of course be iterated. Anderson claimed that it solves $x^x = d$ more easily than $x^3 = d$.

Example. Solve $x^3 - 2x = 5$. Here $x = 2$ is a good start: therefore put $x = 2(1+y)/(1-y)$: whence

$$1 = 43y + 13y^2 + 9y^3.$$

Thus $y = \dfrac{1}{43}$ to a first approximation, and next $y = 1/(43+13y)$ $= 43/(43^2+13) = 43/1862$. This gives $x = 3810/1819 = 2{\cdot}094557\ldots$, which is within $\cdot 00001$ of the true result $2{\cdot}09455148\ldots$.

Maclaurin's Method. After taking an approximate value a, put $x = a+y$, so that y is small. Proceed as before but retain powers of y beyond the second if neces-

* G. Anderson (1739), Letter to Jones, Rigaud's *Correspondence of Scientific Men* (1841).

sary. Iterate. The process is more laborious than Anderson's to the same accuracy.

Example. For $x^3-15x^2+63x-50=0$ take $x=1+y$ where y is small. This gives $1=36y-12y^2+y^3$ or $y=1/(36-12y+y^2)$. Hence $y=1/36$ nearly, and, better still,

$$y=1/\left(36-\frac{12}{36}+\frac{1}{36^2}\right)=\cdot 02803.$$ On putting $y=\cdot 02803+z$ and solving for z but neglecting z^2 and higher terms, the result is $x=1\cdot 02803923127$ very nearly.

71. Newton's Limits for the Roots. After stating in the *Arithmetica Universalis* * the rules for the sums s_p of powers of the roots (as quoted on p. 72), Newton gave a series of interesting theorems including the following: (1) $\sqrt[r]{s_r}\to a$ the greatest root as $r\to\infty$, (2) $s_{r-1}\,s_{r+1}>s_r^{\,2}$ when r is odd, (3) $\sqrt[r]{[\frac{1}{2}\sqrt{(s_{r-1}\,s_{r+1})}+\frac{1}{2}s_r]}\to a$. Newton confined these to equations all whose roots were real. These investigations so early in the development of the subject are interesting, particularly when they are compared with the results given above, using the h and e symmetric functions. The limit of s_{r+1}/s_r could equally well have been used (which would have led to a new but more complicated type of determinantal series on the basis of (7) p. 74), but, on the contrary, the rth root of h_r would not tend to a limit.

Newton's rule, given above on p. 97, follows in the *Arithmetica* immediately after this discussion of s_r.

72. Newton's Rule of Signs. To discover the complex roots Newton thereupon gave a generalization of Descartes' rule of signs which runs as follows: from the equation

$$f(x)=a_0x^n+na_1x^{n-1}+n_{(2)}a_2x^{n-2}+\ldots+na_{n-1}x+a_n=0$$

form the *real* simple elements $a_0, a_1, a_2, \ldots, a_n$ stripped of

* I. Newton, *Universal Arithmetic*, translated by Raphson, revised by Wilder, 1769. (Maclaurin's method, p. 505.)

their binomial coefficients. Then form the quadratic elements, namely

$$A_0 = a_0^2,\ A_1 = a_1^2 - a_0a_2,\ A_2 = a_2^2 - a_1a_3,\ \ldots,\ A_n = a_n^2.$$

Let $\left.\begin{matrix} a_r \\ A_r \end{matrix}\right\}$ form an *associated couple* and $\left.\begin{matrix} a_r\ a_{r+1} \\ A_r\ A_{r+1} \end{matrix}\right\}$ an *associated couple of successions* $a_r\, a_{r+1}$ and $A_r\, A_{r+1}$. Let p, P, v, V respectively denote a permanence or variation of sign in a succession of small or capital letters. There are evidently four possibilities in an associated couple, pP, vV, pV and vP.

Newton's Rule :—

(1) The number of negative roots $\leqslant \Sigma pP$.
(2) The number of positive roots $\leqslant \Sigma vP$.
(3) The number of complex roots $\geqslant \Sigma V$.

This rule was first proved by Sylvester,* nearly two centuries later, who incidentally pointed out that (1) follows at once from (2) on changing x to $-x$ in $f(x)$, while (3) follows from (1) and (2) directly since $\Sigma pP + \Sigma vP = \Sigma P = n - \Sigma V$. Newton adapted the rule to the case when some of the a_i vanished. The inequalities are necessary, " but," says Newton, " you may know almost by this rule how many roots are impossible."

Examples.

1. In $x^3+3x^2+12x+9 = 0$ the a and A series are 1, 1, 4, 9 and 1, -3, 7, 81 respectively, with two variations V of sign in A. Hence at least two complex roots.

2. In $x^3+6x^2+9x-16 = 0$ the signs are

a	+	+	+	−
A	+	+	+	+

giving $\Sigma V = 0$. But there are two complex roots.

* J. J. Sylvester, *Proc. London Math. Soc.*, **1** (1865-1866), p. 1. *Cf. Collected Works*, **2**, p. 498.

73. Note on the Approximate Method of Newton (p. 92). The success of Newton's method for evaluating a real root α of the equation $f(x) = 0$ near a point $x = a$ depends upon the shape of the curve in the neighbourhood of the point Z where it cuts the axis of x. We must assume that neither $f'(x)$ nor $f''(x)$ vanishes throughout the range of values of x corresponding to this neighbourhood. The first condition ensures that $f(x)/f'(x)$ can be evaluated at any point of the range, since its denominator never vanishes, and the second condition excludes a point of inflexion from the arc. This arc is therefore wholly convex upwards ($f''(x)<0$) or wholly convex downwards ($f''(x)>0$) : and therefore must be convex towards the axis of x on one side of Z while being concave towards this axis on the other. Convexity towards the axis of x is indeed the necessary and sufficient condition for the method to succeed. In the first figure (p. 92) this convexity occurs to the left of Z and the successive approximations b, c, .. onwards from $x = b$ at B, form a monotonically increasing sequence whose limit is α. In the second figure (p. 93) the convexity occurs to the right of Z, and the sequence a, b, c, .. onwards from $x = a$ at A is monotonically decreasing to its limit α.

To start at a point A (p. 92) from the concave side at once leads to a next point B on the convex side of Z; but this does not guarantee that B lies within the stipulated neighbourhood. It may or may not. Not only might BZ exceed ZA, but there might also be a point of inflexion on the arc between Z and Q, which would vitiate the next approximation.

Analytically the above condition implies that **within the range of convexity** $f(x)$ **and** $f''(x)$ **must have the same sign** (giving four cases, two with positive $f'(x)$ as illustrated by the figures, and two with negative). The condition is therefore necessary.

It is also sufficient. For, in the case when each of $f(x)$,

$f'(x)$ and $f''(x)$ is positive, we have $a>b>c>..>\alpha$. By the fundamental property of convergence the sequence of such terms $a, b, c, ..$ must tend to a limit l which is either greater than α or is α itself. This implies that the series $\Sigma(f(x)/f'(x))$, where x takes the successive values $a, b, c, ..$, converges to the value $a-l$, since the series Σ can also be written $(a-b)+(b-c)+ \ldots$ Now if $l>\alpha$, take $m = f(l)/f'(a)$ which is positive. Since $f(x)$ exceeds $f(l)$ and $f'(a)$ exceeds $f'(x)$ within the range, each term of the above series exceeds this positive constant m, and the series must therefore fail to converge. Hence $l = \alpha$ only, which proves the result. Similarly for the other cases.

It follows that, however poor the original approximation is, the error will eventually become small. We can now prove that if h is such a small error at a given stage of the sequence, the next successive errors are of orders h^2, h^4, h^8, .. : that is, each error is of order equal to the square of its predecessor. This shows a remarkably high rate of approximation.

To prove this, let $\alpha = a+h$, where a is now quite near to the root α, and h is a positive or negative error. Then

$$0 = f\,(a+h) = f(a)+h\,f'(a)+\tfrac{1}{2}h^2 f''(a+\theta h)$$

where $0<\theta<1$. By the convexity conditions both $f''(a+\theta h)$ and $f'(a)$ are finite and nonzero, so that

$$h = -\frac{f(a)}{f'(a)} - \tfrac{1}{2}h^2\frac{f''(a+\theta h)}{f'(a)} = -\frac{f(a)}{f'(a)} + O(h^2).$$

But $b = a-f(a)/f'(a)$; and $\alpha-a$, $\alpha-b$, which are h, $O(h^2)$, are the two successive errors. The result follows.

Examples.

1. Obtain the Newtonian sequence for the equation $x^2 = 2$, starting with $a = 1$.

$$\left[1, \frac{3}{2}, \frac{17}{12}, \frac{577}{408}, \ldots\right]$$

2. Identify the above fractions as the first, second, fourth, eighth, ..., 2^n-th convergents to the recurring continued fraction

$$\sqrt{2} = 1+\frac{1}{2+}\,\frac{1}{2+}\,\dots.$$

3. Investigate the sequence for the equation
$x^3-3x^2+2x = 0$, starting near the root 1 with $a = 1{\cdot}1$.
[The convexity condition is violated. The process leads to a more remote root zero. Draw a figure.]

4. Show that for the equation $\sin x = 0$ the process breaks down for every value of a.

For further information on this and still more powerful approximations to the root of an equation the reader should consult a recent paper by Dr H. W. Richmond, F.R.S., in the *Journal London Math. Soc.* **19** (1944) 31-38. It is there shewn that the tangents PB, QC, etc., may be replaced by arcs of hyperbolas or higher curves which improve the rapidity of approximation. Thus a hyperbola with three-point contact would cube the error at each stage, in contrast to the tangent line which squares the error.

SUGGESTIONS FOR FURTHER READING

BURNSIDE and PANTON, *Theory of Equations*, I. and II. Dublin. 1899.

WHITTAKER and ROBINSON, *The Calculus of Observations*. Glasgow. 1924.

TURNBULL, *Theory of Determinants, Matrices and Invariants*. Glasgow. 1928.

ALBERT, *Modern Higher Algebra*. Chicago. 1937.

INDEX

PRINTED IN GREAT BRITAIN BY OLIVER AND BOYD LTD., EDINBURGH